The twentieth century has seen biology come of age as a conceptual and quantitative science. Major functional phenomena rather than catalogues of animals and plants comprise the core of MODERN BIOLOGY; such heretofore seemingly unrelated fields as cytology, biochemistry, and genetics are now being unified into a common framework at the molecular level.

The purpose of this Series is to introduce the beginning student in college biology—as well as the gifted high school student and all interested readers—both to the concepts unifying the fields of biology and to the diversity of facts that give the entire field its unique texture. Each book in the Series is an introduction to one of the major foundation stones in the mosaic. Taken together, they provide an integration of the general and the comparative, the cellular and the organismic, the animal and the plant, the structural and the functional—in sum, a solid overview of the dynamic science that is MODERN BIOLOGY.

MODERN BIOLOGY SERIES

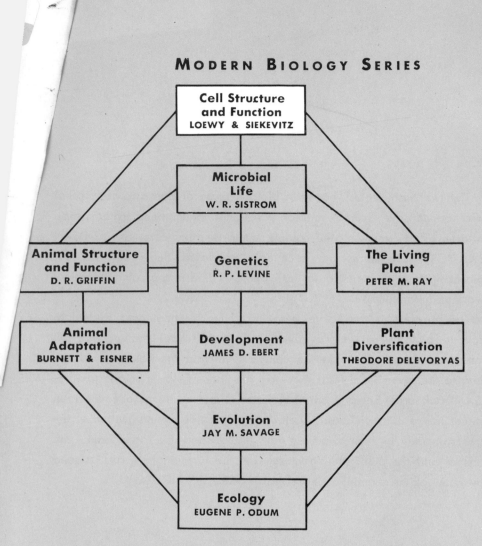

Cell Structure and Function
LOEWY & SIEKEVITZ

Microbial Life
W. R. SISTROM

Animal Structure and Function
D. R. GRIFFIN

Genetics
R. P. LEVINE

The Living Plant
PETER M. RAY

Animal Adaptation
BURNETT & EISNER

Development
JAMES D. EBERT

Plant Diversification
THEODORE DELEVORYAS

Evolution
JAY M. SAVAGE

Ecology
EUGENE P. ODUM

HOLT, RINEHART AND WINSTON

NEW YORK - CHICAGO - SAN FRANCISCO - TORONTO - LONDON

CELL

STRUCTURE

AND

FUNCTION

ARIEL G. LOEWY

HAVERFORD COLLEGE

PHILIP SIEKEVITZ

THE ROCKEFELLER INSTITUTE

THE HARMONIOUS CO-OPERATION OF ALL
BEINGS AROSE, NOT FROM THE ORDERS OF A
SUPERIOR AUTHORITY EXTERNAL TO THEM-
SELVES, BUT FROM THE FACT THAT THEY
WERE ALL PARTS IN A HIERARCHY OF
WHOLES FORMING A COSMIC PATTERN, AND
WHAT THEY OBEYED WERE THE INTERNAL
DICTATES OF THEIR OWN NATURES.

CHUANG TZU
(*Third Century* B.C.)

Cover photograph, *Globigerina,* courtesy of
the American Museum of Natural History

PREFACE

The past decade has witnessed an explosive accumulation of insights into the molecular machinery of the cell.

We are beginning to discern a molecular pattern that includes such phenomena as the self-duplication of the cellular hereditary material and the control it exerts in the formation of the catalysts of the cell. Biological specificity, a property so characteristic of the world of life, is in the process of being related to the structure and interaction of macromolecules. The electron microscope has suddenly created a new world, rich and intricate in detail, which is actively being interpreted in molecular terms. The regulation of this very complicated cellular machinery is now beginning to be examined in a manner that, at the very least, has operational rigor.

These developments have resulted in the realization that there is an inextricable relationship between cellular structure and cellular function. The more classical disciplines of cytology, cell physiology, biochemistry, and biophysics are becoming fused into one common structure that is often referred to as the "molecular biology of the cell."

The purpose of this book is to document these exciting developments and to make them accessible to the introductory student. It is our conviction that since the cell is the "common denominator" of living systems, it is extremely important that the beginner should become acquainted with the major facts and theories of cell biology. This introduction will serve a dual purpose: it will provide the student with a firm basis from which to examine the other manifold phenomena of the world of life, and it will also serve to convince him, at an early stage of his development, of the crucial importance of the physical sciences to the study of living systems.

Because of its limited size, this book both omits certain topics and treats others with unavoidable brevity. However, the material contained in the suggested readings at the end of chapters will considerably broaden the scope of the text proper.

It was not the intention of the authors to make this an "elementary" book in the sense of limiting it necessarily to the simpler and more accessible aspects of cell biology. Yet we hope that it is a book for beginners because we believe it is precisely the beginner who deserves an initial statement that is fully representative of the contemporary quality and mode of the field.

A.G.L.
P.S.

Haverford, Pennsylvania
New York City
June, 1963

CONTENTS

PART I

CELL
BIOLOGY

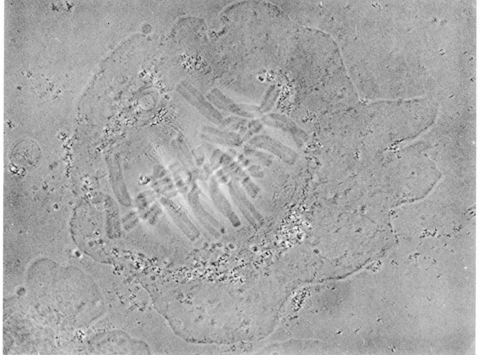

Mitotic spindle as seen by polarizing microscope. The mitotic spindle fibers that pull the chromosomes apart are seen as bright streaks. *Top:* Oöcyte of marine worm, *Chaetopterus pergamentaceous. Bottom:* Endosperm cell from the fruit of African blood lily, *Haemanthus katherinae.* Chromosome pairs are just about to be separated. (Photographs courtesy of S. Inoué, Dartmouth Medical School, and of *Chromosoma.)*

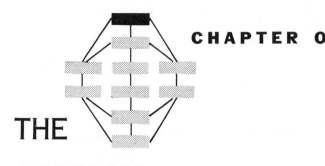

CHAPTER ONE

THE COMMON DENOMINATOR OF LIVING

MATTER The study of the world of life is as old as man himself, for the classification and comparison of the prodigious diversity of living forms is intimately connected with man's survival. Our ancestors were aware of the differences between a bat and a bird long before they had an inkling that there were similarities between the tissues of a mushroom and a man.

The awareness that all organisms share certain common principles dates back to the cell theory. This theory, enunciated by Schleiden and Schwann in 1838, stated that all living systems are composed of cells and of cell products. Today this statement may seem to be self-evident, but we must not forget that we have lived with this scientific truth for a long time. To Schleiden and Schwann's predecessors, the concept that the organism is the fundamental unit of biological activity was an easily observable, well-established, common-sense principle. That organisms are in turn composed of smaller subunits each of which is endowed with an individual identity must have been a revelation of first magnitude. Indeed, the extent to which the cell has an individuality of its own and a capability of independent existence was by no means clear even to Schleiden and Schwann. It is only in recent years that we have begun to recognize the degree to which all cells share a large portion of the principles we call the "machinery of life." We have learned that cells, whether they are protozoans or human liver cells, duplicate their genetic material in the same way, utilize their hereditary information to

3

synthesize proteins in the same way, handle the transfer of energy in the same way, regulate the exchange of materials in the same way, convert chemical energy into work in the same way, and so on. In fact, it has been disconcerting to those interested in differentiation or in the problem of cancer that so few fundamental differences can be detected between cells of various types.

The purpose of this book is to describe the common features of the machinery of the cell, because we believe that it is the basic "module," the common denominator of all the immense variety of living forms. One must not forget, however, that all cells have specialized roles over the entire range of diversity in biological form and function; the generalized cell we are about

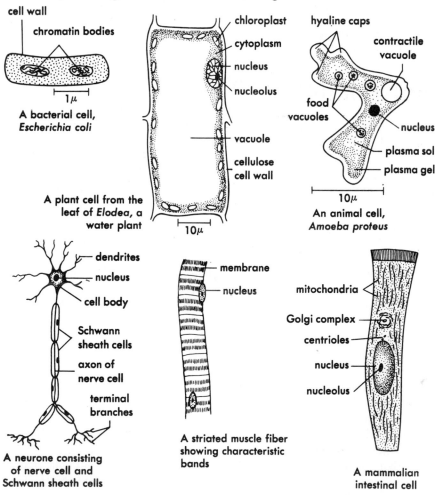

Fig. 1-1. A number of cell types found in the microbial, plant, and animal kingdoms.

to describe is an abstraction that does not exist as such in nature. Instead, special cells adapted for specific functions are found (Fig. 1-1): the simple unicellular microorganism with its short generation time and rapidly adapting metabolism; the plant cell with its large vacuole and thin cellulose wall maintaining structural rigidity through its osmotic balance with the environment; and the animal cell, naked and often mobile, capable of ingesting large particles of food. Within each of these three major kingdoms and even within each given organism are numerous different cell types (Fig. 1-1). The mammalian body, for instance, contains the elongated and fibrillar, striated muscle cell, the slender and branched nerve cell, and the metabolically active intestinal cell. These and many more represent specializations that adapt cells to their specific roles. It is not within the scope of this book to do more than refer on occasion to these specialized functions. However, it is important to recognize that many specialized cell functions find their origin in general cellular phenomena occurring in attenuated form throughout the cellular world. Nerve conduction is based on action potentials that occur in all cells. Muscular contraction is based on a mechanism of conversion of chemical energy into work, which appears to occur universally. Osmotic work found, for instance, in a highly active form in kidney cells also appears to be a universal property of living matter. Thus even if no generalized or archetypal cell exists, it is convenient to create one to serve as a conceptual model within which most cell functions can be incorporated and discussed.

Our discussion of the archetypal cell will, like most experimental approaches to biology, rest on the presupposition that biological phenomena can be analyzed in terms of physical and chemical principles. This admittedly is an act of faith that cannot be justified on a priori grounds; yet it is an eminently *useful* act of faith and represents the philosophical basis of an approach that is yielding communicable and verifiable results of ever-widening significance with ever-increasing rapidity. Indeed it is the purpose of this book to document the explosive growth of the molecular approach to cell biology.

SUGGESTED READING LIST

BOURNE, G. H., 1962. *Division of labor in cells.* New York: Academic Press.

BRACHET, J., "The living cell," *Scientific American*, September 1961.

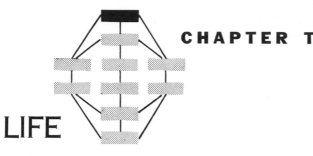

CHAPTER TWO

LIFE AND THE SECOND LAW OF THERMODYNAMICS

It has been estimated that between two and four billion years ago life started on our planet. Whether life started spontaneously from nonliving matter, or whether it came to our planet in the form of spores seeded throughout the universe by distant solar systems, we don't know. In either case we might suppose that life first began by the transformation of nonliving materials into living matter. There have been many speculations in recent years on the mechanism involved in such a remarkable transformation.

We have said that the living has come from the nonliving. This presupposes that there is a difference between these two states of matter, and it is therefore legitimate to ask what the difference might be. A *complete* definition of living matter is not yet possible, for this involves a complete knowledge and understanding of it. Nevertheless, since we are usually able to distinguish between "animal, vegetable, and mineral," it is logical to ask ourselves upon what criteria such judgments are based. Are there any unique criteria of living matter? We usually answer this question by listing a number of characteristics that we associate with living matter, such as movement, reproduction, metabolism, sensitivity, growth, etc. It is generally admitted that each of these properties can be found in the nonliving world, but it is argued that in living matter they are present simultaneously and find their most complex degree of expression. Thus it is true that locomotives work, computers think, and some automated machines can reproduce. So far we do not have computers that dig ditches, reproduce, enjoy poetry, and make moral judgments. But if we are committed to the notion that living matter is subject to the laws of chemistry and physics, then we must accept the possibility that such monsters can, in principle, be built. Are we to conclude that there need be no essential difference between the man and the monster? We think yes, but with one crucial proviso: the historical origins of man and monster are different. Man built the monster and not vice versa. We emerge, then, with a criterion of living matter that is historical in character. Life is that process which started at an uncomplicated level and which has spontaneously gained in complexity through a process we call evolution. This process has taken a long time and finds its present most complex expression in the form of *Homo sapiens*. The above-mentioned ever-expanding organization is at present being extended by *Homo sapiens* to his physical surroundings so that different forms of organization, both concrete (buildings, machines, etc.) and abstract (knowledge, insight, and even wisdom), are being accumulated at an increasing rate. Whether this new form of extra-organismic organization we call civilization is evolutionarily stable, leading to undreamed-of developments in the social evolution of man, or whether it is permeated with biologically rooted contradictions incapable of solution at a social level, only the future will determine.

In spite of the recent great achievements in the construction of highly complicated mechanical devices able to carry out many operations hitherto restricted to living matter, we must not underrate the intricate organization of living systems. The almost infinitesimally minute scale into which biological organization is capable of being compressed is one of the most dazzling wonders of nature. One need only compare the monstrous electronic computers powered by megawatts of energy with the infinitely more sophisticated human brain powered by mere microwatts of energy, to recognize the remarkable spatial and energetic economy with which biological systems operate. The fact that the human sperm is able to carry in its tiny volume half of all the genetic determinants of the mature individual is another example of the degree of "microminiaturization" accomplished by living matter. Our engineers have yet to learn this intriguing trick of nature.

We have said so far that the fundamental characteristic of the world of life is the evolution, maintenance, and extension of a tremendous degree of organization, capable of being compressed into tiny volumes. Is this process of organization, maintenance, and extension a unique property of living matter? The Second Law of Thermodynamics, a fundamental law of the physical universe, states that systems in isolation spontaneously tend toward states of greater disorganization. At first glance it would seem that the Second Law is not obeyed by living matter, and indeed this is what G. N. Lewis, one of the creators of thermodynamic theory, suspected. However, in order to examine this problem more carefully, we must make a more precise statement of the Second Law of Thermodynamics. The degree of disorganization, or entropy, of a system is not the only property involved in a spontaneous process. The "free energy" is an important parameter and can be defined as "energy capable of performing work." A process can only proceed spontaneously when there is a loss of free energy. In an isolated system at constant temperature, the change in free energy and the change in entropy are related to each other by the following equation:

$$\Delta F = \Delta H - T \Delta S$$

where

ΔF is the change in free energy
ΔH is the change in heat content, or enthalpy
T is the absolute temperature
ΔS is the change in entropy

Although the Second Law of Thermodynamics began as an empirical generalization, it has since been possible to account for it by applying statistical methods of analysis to the particles of which matter is composed.

Although the Second Law predicts that a system when left to itself will tend to decrease its state of organization, it nevertheless allows for an increase in organization when free energy is supplied to the system. And this is what seems to occur in the case of living matter. The high free-energy content and low state of disorganization of living matter are maintained and at times even extended by a constant supply of free energy. As soon as this supply of free energy is cut off, living systems proceed spontaneously to a greater state of disorganization (death). This type of labile system that is maintained at a certain level of organization by a continuous supply of free energy is often described as a *steady state*. It does not represent an *equilibrium* in which the system has achieved the lowest possible free energy and the highest possible disorganization. In fact, a steady state is a system *away* from equilibrium, which can only be maintained in this apparent constancy by the continuous supply of free energy. A physical model for such a situation might be a thermoregulated water bath maintaining a constant temperature different from that of its environment. Here again is a physical model differing from its living equivalent (that is, the temperature regulation of a mammal) primarily in its historical origin. It is, after all, we who built the constant temperature bath.

A constant supply of free energy is only one requirement for the maintenance of a steady state. There must also be a minimal organization capable of absorbing and channeling the energy in a usable manner. As biologists we believe that in the case of the history of living organisms, this organization has appeared by a series of chance events linked to each other in a progression of constantly increasing complexity by the phenomenon of natural selection. We believe that this phenomenon of emergent evolution does not violate the Second Law of Thermodynamics, since it was "powered" by a continuous and generous supply of free energy finding its origin in the atomic reactions of the sun. With the advent of human intelligence the evolution of various types of organization—be it a library, a scientific theory, or a computer—can no longer be considered quite as random as the genetic mutations are believed to be, but here too the general principle holds; namely, that free energy is necessary to permit the elaboration of these products of the human imagination.

Five billion years ago, before life had begun on our planet, all the free energy poured on it by the sun was rapidly dissipated as useless heat and radiated into outer space. Then tiny systems evolved, capable of trapping some of the free energy, which was used to maintain and extend the organization of these systems. As evolution proceeded, this trapping process became more efficient and extensive. Today, the trapped rays of the sun are supplying the free energy to build cities or to turn living matter on itself in the investigation of the principles by which it is governed. The steady state of life has acquired some of the free energy of the sun and is holding it in the form of an ever-expanding "biosphere."

There is a Third Law of Thermodynamics that states that, at absolute zero temperature, the entropy of every substance is zero. We should perhaps enunciate a "fourth law," which would state that, given plenty of time, the necessary atomic building blocks, the right temperature, and a steady supply of free energy possibly fluctuating in a diurnal cycle, a "bios" of increasing complexity will of necessity develop, which has the over-all effect of decreasing the rate at which free energy becomes degraded. The current views held by astronomers that the suns of the universe are likely to be accompanied by planets of which a finite number are similar to the planet earth, lead us to the conviction that we are not alone in this universe. We no longer think of evolution as the "great coincidence," but as a full-fledged law of nature.

We conclude that living matter is not outside the physical world, but an integral part of it. It is a fascinating special case of physical matter, distinguished by the long and characteristic history of its development.

SUGGESTED READING LIST

BLUM, H. F., 1955. *Time's arrow and evolution*. Princeton, N.J.: Princeton University Press.

OPARIN, A. I., 1961. *Life, its nature, origin and development*. New York: Academic Press.

PENROSE, L. S., "Self-reproducing machines," *Scientific American*, June 1959.

UREY, H., "The origin of the earth," *Scientific American*, October 1952.

WALD, G., "The origin of life," *Scientific American*, August 1956.

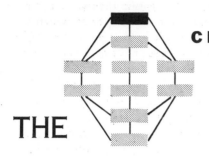

CHAPTER THREE

THE
NATURAL
HISTORY
OF THE
CELL

The cell is the biological unit of activity. Though it is divisible into subcellular particles that retain some of the properties of the original functioning unit, the cell nevertheless represents a minimum unit of relatively independent activity. It is the smallest portion of the organism that exhibits the *range of properties* we have come to associate with living material. In this chapter we shall deal with this range of properties in order to give the reader a feeling for the "personality" of the cell.

CELL SIZE AND SHAPE

In the world of mathematics an equation remains unchanged if both sides are enlarged in the same proportion. This is not true in the physical world, where relationships between objects are very much influenced by their absolute dimensions. It is obvious that the expanding and shrinking world of Lewis Carroll's Alice is the product of the imagination of a mathematician, not that of a physicist or biologist. One of the early investigators of size and shape in biological systems was the British biologist D'Arcy Thompson, who pointed out, for example, that an elephant of twice the weight would have to be supported by leg bones of four times the cross-sectional area. In spite of D'Arcy Thompson's widely read, interesting book, biologists

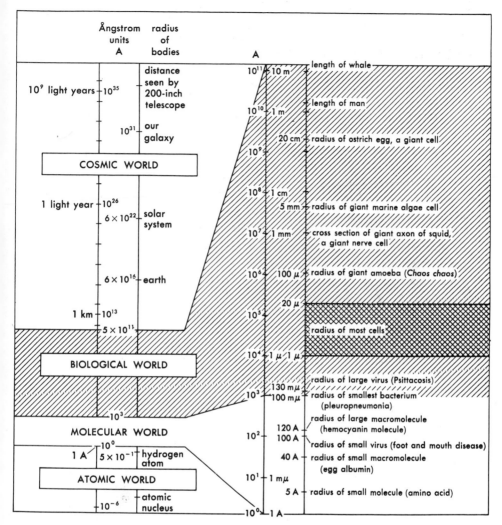

Fig. 3-1. Size relationships at the atomic, molecular, biological, and cosmic levels.

on the whole have been slow in recognizing the significance of absolute dimensions. And yet the world of life falls into a size range that from a cosmic viewpoint is restricted to a narrow band of magnitude. Fig. 3-1 is a summary of the size relationships observed on a cosmic, biological, and atomic level. It illustrates the fact that biological systems fall into definite and overlapping size ranges. Thus, for example, the largest cell is larger than the smallest mammal, the largest virus larger than the smallest cell, and the largest macromolecule larger than the smallest virus.

If cells fall into a certain size range, what are the laws governing this fact? We shall, for the sake of convenience, define a *cell* as *a unit of biological activity delimited by a semipermeable membrane and capable of self-reproduction in a medium free of other living systems.* A *virus* we shall define as *a self-reproductive biological unit that does not have a finite semipermeable membrane and is capable of self-reproduction only within a living cell.*

The smallest living cells are found among the bacteria. Species as small as spheres 250 mμ in diameter have been observed. (1000 microns [μ] = 1 millimeter [mm]; 1000 millimicrons [mμ] = 1μ.) In the pleuropneumonia-like organisms, so-called "elementary bodies" have been observed with diameters of 100 mμ. These appear to be a resting form of the bacterium, which may grow into bodies 250 mμ in diameter during the active metabolism of the organism. It would seem that 200 to 250 mμ in diameter is the lower limit for the size of an active, living cell. This lower limit may well be set by the minimum number and size of the components necessary for independent cellular existence. The volume of a cell 200 mμ in diameter will be approximately 4×10^6 mμ^3. Assuming that 80 percent of the cell is water, this leaves a "dry volume" of 8×10^5 mμ^3. The bulkiest components of the cell are the macromolecules, the proteins and nucleic acids, many of which have a diameter in the range of 5 to 20 mμ. Assuming an average diameter of 10 mμ, we obtain an average volume per macromolecule of 5×10^2 mμ^3. Ignoring the bulk of cellular components other than proteins and nucleic acids, and dividing the average volume of the macromolecules into the dry volume of the cell, we find that there is room for only 1600 macromolecules. Assuming that there are a minimum of 500 metabolic reactions necessary for independent existence and that each step involves the existence of one deoxyribonucleic acid, DNA (gene), one ribonucleic acid, RNA ("messenger"), and one protein (enzyme) macromolecule, it would appear that in these smallest of cells there is room only for one or two of each of the necessary macromolecules. This is a remarkable conclusion, for it illustrates the fact that the cell is able to behave in a reproducible and predictable fashion utilizing macromolecules each type of which is present in an "unstatistical" quantity.

The problems affecting the upper limit in cell size are very different. First of all it must be recognized that although the vast majority of cells lie in the range of 0.5 to 20μ in diameter, there are some truly giant cells, the existence of which is related to some very special biological circumstance. The conditions that affect the upper limit in cell size seem to be relational ones. First, there is the relation between the nucleus and the rest of the cell. As we shall see later, there is evidence that the nucleus releases certain "messengers" that determine the synthesis of the cell's proteins. Clearly this will determine the amount of cytoplasm a given nucleus can "control." Some cells manage to transcend this limitation by being multinucleate, like the giant cells of the amoeba *Chaos chaos* or the green alga *Nitella*. Second, there is the relationship between the various parts of the cell. The larger the cell the greater the problem of diffusion. In large multinucleate cells like *Nitella* or in the *slime molds* this problem is solved by a very active form of protoplasmic streaming. Third, there is the relationship between the cell and its environment. The plasma membrane is an extremely impermeable layer. The larger the cell the smaller the surface-volume ratio becomes. This factor has a tendency to isolate the cell from its environment, a situation that the cell sometimes overcomes by a number of anatomical modifications. The enlargement of the surface area by extensive invagination is one device. Another anatomical feature, found in nerve cells, which in larger animals can be several feet long, is the development of a threadlike geometry. In a long, thin thread the increase in surface area remains proportional to volume and thus the degree of contact between the cell and its environment is not reduced.

It can be seen from the above discussion that cell shape is intimately related to cell function. This relationship in itself is a topic of gigantic proportions in comparative cell biology and is well beyond the scope of this volume.

CELL FUNCTION

A living system is a locus of behavior. That this behavior has a structural basis is a principle we consider to be the central theme of this book. But ultimately it is the *behavior* of the units of life that comes closest to characterizing their nature, and it is therefore fitting that we preface our description of cell anatomy with a very generalized discussion of cell function.

As we stated in the previous chapter, living matter represents a high degree of organization (low entropy) kept in a labile, steady-state condition by a continuous supply of free energy. At the same time (and this would seem to be a fundamental aspect of such systems) a complex organization is needed to funnel energy into channels useful for the *maintenance* of organization. Thus energy is needed for the maintenance of organization, and organization is needed for the proper utilization of energy.

Fig. 3-2 is a flow diagram summarizing in very general terms the energy transformations of the cell. It should be noted that plants and animals resemble each other closely except with respect to the ultimate source of energy upon which they must rely. The plant uses light energy to manufacture carbohydrates, fats, and proteins whereas the animal ingests these substances as foods. The carbohydrates, fats, and proteins are not the immediate fuels that run the cell's machines; instead, ATP (adenosine triphosphate) performs this function. The energy released by the respiratory metabolism of the cell, in which carbohydrates, fats, and proteins are broken down

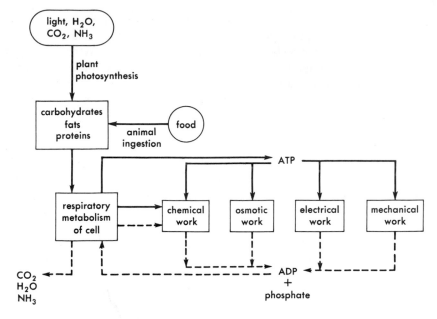

Fig. 3-2. The flow of energy through living systems. Solid lines refer to "high-energy" content and dashed lines low-energy content.

into carbon dioxide, water, and ammonia, is utilized in a number of steps to convert ADP (adenosine diphosphate) into ATP (see Chapter 11).

To summarize, carbohydrates, fats, and proteins are the "crude fuels" used to generate the "high grade" fuel ATP, which in turn runs all the machines of the cell. What are these machines of the cell and what function do they perform?

Chemical Work (see Chapters 13 and 14)

The machine we have labeled in Fig. 3-2 as performing chemical work is in reality many separate machines a few of which we are beginning to understand.

Unlike the machines we build, the cell has to carry out the combustion of carbohydrates, fats, and proteins in a structural matrix composed of the same materials. Thus the cell must constantly *replace* components that have become altered during their function. Furthermore, one of the major facts of life is that living matter always extends itself. The cell not only repairs itself, it also *duplicates* (see Chapter 12). We do not know whether this is a physiological necessity or an evolutionary consequence of natural selection, but whichever the origin, the fact remains that a great deal of the energy funneled into a cell is utilized for growth and cell duplication. The concept of the *hereditary material* is necessary to the understanding of how the cell performs these vital functions.

It has been recognized for a long time that the cell does not build all of its components from "scratch." A certain proportion of its structural organization is retained from generation to generation. This portion of the material of the cell is called the *hereditary material*, and it is characterized by the fact that it is involved in its own synthesis (see Chapter 12). The hereditary material would be of no use, however, if that were its only function. Besides this role of self-duplication it also initiates the physiological functions that the cell performs. A great deal of negative entropy (organization) of the cell is located in the hereditary material, and the cell has to expend energy both in duplicating it as well as in carrying out its directives regarding physiological function and growth.

Osmotic Work (see Chapter 15)

We have already said that living material differs greatly from its environment in the relative abundance and also the absolute concentration of its component parts. To bring about and maintain this situation, the cell must perform osmotic work. It must perform work both to accumulate materials found in low concentrations in its environment as well as to remove from within it materials found in high concentration in its surrounding medium. But not only do accumulation and elimination require work; so also does the *maintenance* of this thermodynamically improbable situation. In fact, this process of maintenance would be impossible in terms of energy were it not for the presence of the plasma membrane, which, by creating an extremely tight barrier to diffusion, saves the cell a great deal of energy.

Electrical Work (see Chapter 15)

The cell's plasma membrane is never equally permeable to specific cations and anions, nor are they ever accumulated to the same extent. For these reasons all cells will exhibit a slight separation of charge across their membrane, leaving the outside positive with respect to the inside or vice versa. This electrical difference is utilized in nerve cells for communication, by the transmission of an electric impulse in the form of a breakdown in charge separation. This activity, like any other form of work, requires energy.

Mechanical Work (see Chapter 14)

All of life is connected with motion of some sort, whether it is the contraction of muscle cells, the beat of cilia, the flow of the amoeba, the cyclosis of the protoplasm in a plant cell, or the movement of chromosomes. Motion requires energy funneled into a machine that can convert chemical energy into work.

In addition to these four general categories of energy-requiring activities, cells may engage in a number of other functions that are not quite so universal. Cells interact and influence each other in the growth and development of an organism (see *Development*, in this series) as well as in the physiological functioning of multicellular systems (see *Animal Structure and Function*, in this series). Some cells even produce light! From an evolutionary standpoint perhaps the most significant recent development in the thermodynamics of life is that some of the organization of the cell is transferred outside its cellular limits; that is, living systems can utilize energy to organize their surroundings. This social phase of biological evolution occurs most extensively at the organismic and population levels, and is most evident in human activities.

THE FUNCTIONAL ANATOMY OF THE CELL

We live in the midst of a revolution in cell anatomy—a revolution brought about by the electron microscope, which has given us literally a new picture of the cell, broad in scope and rich in detail (Figs. 3-3, 3-4). A brief description of this valuable instrument is worthwhile here. The visualization of an object depends upon the particular electromagnetic wave utilized. For an object to be "seen" it must absorb or reflect electromagnetic waves of wavelengths no larger than about twice the diameter of the object. This determines the *resolving power* of the microscope, which is defined as the shortest distance between two points that allows them to be observed as separate entities. The resolving power in the light microscope is about 250 $m\mu$, since the lower limit of visible light is about 500 $m\mu$. In the ultraviolet light microscope one can lower the limit of resolution to about 80 $m\mu$ by working with the much shorter wavelengths of ultraviolet light. The electron microscope uses instead of light a beam of electrons with a wavelength of less than one Ångstrom (A; 0.1 $m\mu$). Instead of glass it uses electromagnetic fields as lenses and condensers capable of refracting the beam of electrons, in much the same manner as the classical light microscope handles light. Instead of the retina of the eye, the electron microscope produces the image on a fluorescent screen or a photographic plate. Even though the theoretical resolving power of the electron microscope is less than 1 A, the engineering problems involved in the design of the instrument, as well as the technical problems involved in producing suitable specimens, are enormous and so far resolution of 6 to 8 A has been achieved only infrequently. On the other hand, resolution of 20 to 40 A can be achieved quite readily. The main drawback of the electron microscope, which increases resolving power over light microscopy 100-fold, is that specimens must be "bone dry" and ultrathin. We therefore see only "profiles" of structures that are no longer alive. We re-create a picture of the actual structures in our minds by integrating the profiles.

What, then, is our present picture of the anatomy of the cell as it has been profoundly expanded and modified by the application of the recent techniques?

The cell surface is delimited by a definite, very sharply defined "skin." As we shall see in Chapter 15, this is the osmotically active *plasma membrane*, which is capable of lowering the rate of penetration of molecules as well as discriminating between them. We suspect that the plasma membrane carries catalytically active regions and that the machinery-utilizing energy for carrying out osmotic work is also located here. The plasma membrane is about 75 A thick and appears to be composed of three separate layers (Fig. 15-1). Before the advent of the electron microscope we used to think of the plasma membrane as being stretched tightly over the cell. Now we know that this is usually not the case. The surface of the cell either folds outward to form "microvilli" or it invaginates to form vesicles (Fig. 3-5). These and other modifications of the cell surface are intimately related to the particular osmotic relations of the cell in which they are found. One has the impression that the plasma membrane is a standard, reasonably invariable structure at the molecular level and that it adapts itself to variations in cell function by modifications of its anatomy. As we shall see in Chapter 15, the invaginations often observed at the cell surface seem to give rise, through an inward movement of the plasma membrane, to some of the *vacuoles* appearing in the cell interior (Figs. 3-5 and 15-6). This method of ingesting fluid trapped within the vesicles is called *pinocytosis* (Chap. 15).

If one explores the cell surface in greater detail one discovers that some of the invaginations are not delimited by a vesicle but instead lead right into the depth of the cell (Fig. 15-6). There, channels connect with a complex set of vesicles that interlace the structure of the cell and are called the *endoplasmic reticulum* (Fig. 13-2). The structure and functions of these membranes will be discussed more fully in Chapters 13 and 15. The membrane of the endoplasmic reticulum has the same appearance as the surface plasma membrane. This system of vesicles varies greatly in shape both from one cell type to another, and also in different physiological and developmental stages of the same cell type. The appearance of the endoplasmic reticulum can be "rough" when it carries on its cytoplasmic side numerous, closely spaced granules (diameter 150 A) called *ribosomes* (Figs. 13-2 and 15-6) or it can be "smooth" when the ribosomes are absent (Fig. 15-6).

Examination of the endoplasmic reticulum reveals that it connects with two other structures. First, it is continuous with a system of tightly packed, smooth-surfaced vesicles with a characteristic position in the cell near the

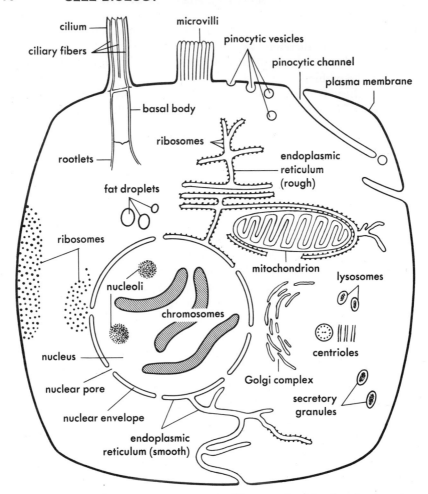

Fig. 3-3. Stylized diagram of a "typical cell" as visualized by the electron microscope. The various structures are not found in all cells, but illustrate the differentiations that occur among cell types.

nucleus. This structure, called the Golgi complex (apparatus), had been an object of controversy for many decades until its existence was finally clearly demonstrated with the electron microscope. The function of the Golgi complex is still largely a mystery, though it has been credited with having a role in the secretion of giant molecules (macromolecules) by the animal cell.

Second, the endoplasmic reticulum membrane is in continuity with the outer of the two membranes that are wrapped around the nucleus (Fig. 15-6). The two-membrane structure has pores, which may or many not be plugged, so that topologically, and possibly physiologically, the inside of the nucleus is continuous with the interior of the cell.

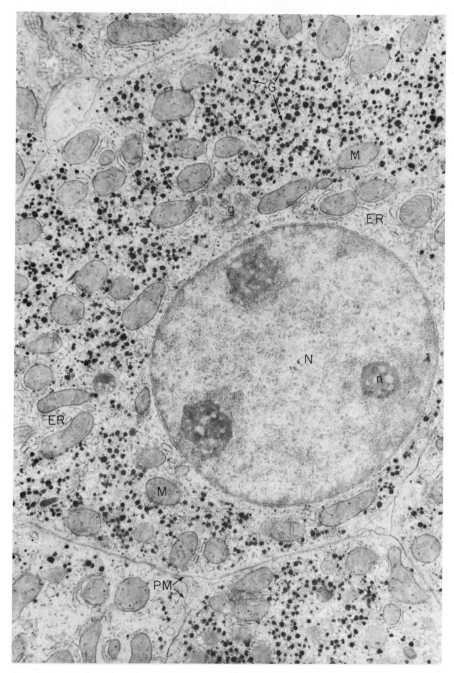

Fig. 3-4. Cell under electron microscope ($\times$ 19,500). An electronmicrograph of a hepatic cell, showing the nucleus (N), with three nucleoli (n), mitochondria (M), profiles of the endoplasmic reticulum (ER), the Golgi zone (g), deposits of glycogen (G), and the plasma membrane (PM). (Courtesy of G. Palade, Rockefeller Institute.)

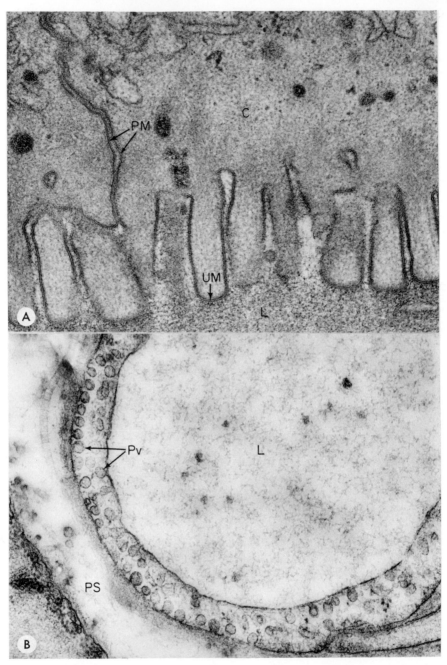

Fig. 3-5. Electronmicrographs of modifications of plasma membrane. A: Microvilli in brush border of intestinal mucosa cell ($\times$ 69,750). B: Pinocytic vesicles observed in endothelial cell of blood capillary in skeletal muscle ($\times$ 46,500). UM, unit membrane; PM, plasma membrane; L, lumen; C, cytoplasm; PS, pericapillary space; Pv, pinocytic vesicles. (Courtesy of Palade.)

So far we have confined our examination to the outside of the cell and that portion of the cell's interior which is continuous with it. If we cross through one thickness of the membrane we find the cell interior, a rich mixture of macromolecules, smaller organic compounds, and ions that comprise the *ground substance* or *cytoplasmic matrix*. This "colloidal" material has the unusual property of being capable both of viscous flow like a liquid and of elastic deformation like a solid. Furthermore it can vary in the degree to which it is one or the other. On the whole, the cytoplasmic matrix near the outer membrane tends to be more like a solid whereas the interior tends to be more liquid. But much depends on the type or physiological state of the cell.

There has been much discussion over the years as to the existence of an organized framework in the ground substance at a submicroscopic level. Although no obvious cytoplasmic skeleton has so far been detected with the electron microscope, we do have certain instances of fibrillar organization in the cytoplasmic matrix. There is for instance the pair of *centrioles* with their beautifully exact and universal organization of "3 × 9" fibers (Fig. 3-6). These two bodies, lying at right angles to each other near the nucleus, appear to be involved in the organization of the *spindle* during nuclear division. Here in the spindle is another example of fibrillar organization in the cytoplasmic matrix, which, as shown in Fig. 3-6, can be seen in living material with the aid of a polarizing microscope (see also photographs on page 2).

Many cells are ciliated or flagellated. These mobile extensions of the cytoplasmic matrix are capable of converting chemical energy into work. It appears that they originate from *kinetosomes*, or *basal bodies*. Both the basal bodies and the cilium itself have a fibrillar organization that closely resembles that of the centriole (Fig. 3-6). The "9 + 2" fibrillar organization of cilia and centrioles has a dramatic uniformity over the entire plant and animal world from the unicellular plant *Euglena* to the sperm of man.

Another example of fibrillar organization in the cytoplasmic matrix is found in the highly specialized muscle cell (Figs. 14-3 and 14-4). Here two types of protein fibers are organized in a highly regular pattern and are presumably responsible for the contractile properties of muscle.

On the whole it would appear that the cytoplasmic matrix is capable of a number of forms of fibrillar organization that seem to be involved in the conversion of chemical energy into mechanical work. Since the rapidly streaming cytoplasm of primitive cells like the slime molds have been shown to contain macromolecules capable of converting chemical energy into work, we conclude that even when no fibrillar structure is visible in the cytoplasm it is possible for submicroscopic elements there to initiate organized activity in the cytoplasm on a macroscopic scale.

The cytoplasmic matrix suspends or surrounds a number of "*organelles*," each of which is enveloped by a membrane. These are the *mitochondria*, the

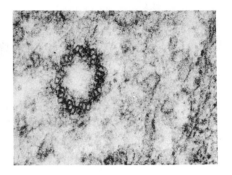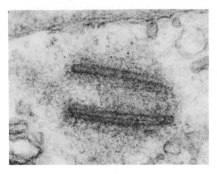

Fig. 3-6. (*Above and facing.*) Some fibrillar organizations of the cytoplasmic matrix, or ground substance. **Above:** Centriole in rat thymus cell. *Left,* cross section; *right,* longitudinal section (× 73,300). (Courtesy of E. de Harven, Rockefeller Institute.) **Facing:** *top,* cilia on the gill of the fresh-water mussel *Anodonta cataracta.* The shaft of the cilia extends outward from the basal bodies of the epithelial cell cytoplasm (× 34,000). (Courtesy of I. Gibbons, Harvard University.) *Bottom left,* cross section of a flagellum from the protozoan *Trichonympha* (× 127,500). (Courtesy of Gibbons.) *Bottom right,* cross section of a basal body in *Trichonympha* (× 127,500) (Courtesy of Gibbons.)

chloroplasts (in green plants), the *lysozomes,* the *nucleus,* and various other bodies or granules, like the *fat granules.*

The *mitochondrion* (see Chapter 11) is a double-membraned structure with the outer membrane stretched tightly around it and the inner membrane invaginating into the body of the organelle as folds, or cristae, to form a huge surface area (Fig. 11-1). The mitochondrion is the center of the cell's respiratory metabolism where the foods of the cell are oxidized to carbon dioxide and water, and the energy released is used to convert ADP into ATP. We suspect that the large area of the inner membrane carries the multitude of enzymes involved in these processes. The location and number of mitochondria in a cell are intimately related to cell function.

The *chloroplasts* are highly organized bodies in green plants and are the centers of photosynthetic activity. A more detailed description of these interesting organelles is found in *The Living Plant,* in this series.

The *lysozomes* are nearly spherical bodies that appear to contain a number of "digestive" enzymes of the cell. The function of these bodies is just beginning to be understood. It has been suggested that they isolate these enzymes from the cell and thus protect it from self-digestion. At cell death, these lysozomes are thought to break down, releasing the digestive enzymes that will then *autolyze* the cell. The enzymes of phagocytic cells may be involved in the digestion of foreign particles like bacteria.

The *nucleus,* as the name implies, is a central or crucial cell organelle. It is the site of a major portion of the cell's hereditary material (see Chap-

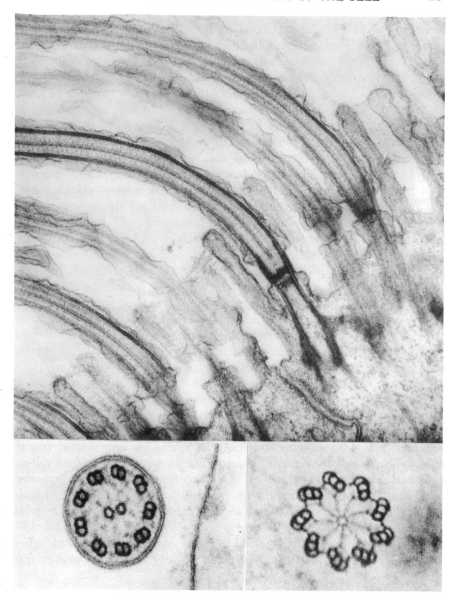

Fig. 3-6.

ter 12). This hereditary material is located on very long and slender threads
(chromosomes) packed relatively tightly in the nucleus, and within the cell
there occurs an ingenious process whereby the self-duplicated chromosomes
are apportioned equally into the two daughter cells (see *Genetics*, in this
series). This process (Fig. 3-7) involves the shortening and thickening of the

SUGGESTED READING LIST

BLOOM, W., and FAWCETT, D. W., 1962. *Textbook of histology*. Philadelphia: Saunders.

BRACHET, J., and MIRSKY, A. E., eds., 1959–1961. *The cell*. New York: Academic Press.

BRACHET, J., 1957. *Biochemical cytology*. New York: Academic Press.

DAVSON, H., 1959. *A textbook of general physiology*. Boston: Little, Brown.

DE ROBERTIS, E. D. P., NOWINSKI, W. W., and SAEZ, F. A., 1960. *General cytology*, 3d ed. Philadelphia: Saunders.

ENGSTROM, A., and FINEAN, J. B., 1958. *Biological ultrastructure*. New York: Academic Press.

GIESE, A. C., 1962. *Cell physiology*, 2d ed. Philadelphia: Saunders.

MAZIA, D., "How cells divide." *Scientific American*, September 1961.

PICKEN, L. E. R., 1960. *The organization of cells and other organisms*. Oxford: Clarendon Press.

THOMPSON, D'ARCY W., 1961. *On growth and form*, abridged ed. Cambridge: Cambridge University Press.

WILSON, E. B., 1928 (reprinted in 1953). *The cell in development and heredity*. New York: Macmillan.

PART II

BIOLOGICAL
STATICS

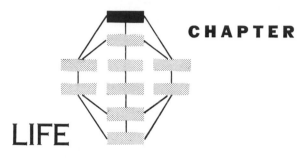

CHAPTER FOUR

LIFE

AND THE

PERIODIC

TABLE A characteristic property of living matter is that it is selec-

tive in its relationship to the environment. An example of this selectivity is the considerable difference between the abundance of available elements on the earth and those found in living organisms. The earth's crust is made mostly of oxygen, silicon, aluminum, sodium, calcium, iron, magnesium, and potassium, the remaining elements constituting less than 1 percent of the total. Living organisms, on the other hand, are made mostly of hydrogen, oxygen, carbon, and nitrogen, with the remaining elements constituting less than 1 percent of the total (Table 4-1). Thus, with the exception of oxygen there is no overlap between the most abundant elements in the earth's crust and those in living matter. Oxygen, with an atomic number of 8, is the heaviest of the major elements of living matter and at the same time the lightest of the major elements of the earth's crust. We conclude that living matter preferentially selects for the light elements made available to it in the earth's crust and atmosphere.

It is remarkable that in this respect living matter is very much like the cosmos as a whole. The stars as well as the interstellar matter are composed mostly of light elements. Our earth is but a "mineral ash" of heavy elements that remained after the light elements distilled into space owing to the weak gravitational pull of tiny earth. Fig. 4-1 shows the parallelism that, with the exception of helium, is found between the first 30 elements in the cosmos and in the living organism. Whether this striking parallelism is coincidental or a form of biological conservation of the chemical composition of the sur-

TABLE 4-1

Relative Abundances of 14 Major Elements
in Universe, Earth's Crust, and Human Body
(Recalculated from Edsall and Wyman)

Element	Atomic number	Relative abundance in atoms percent		
		Universe	Earth's crust	Human body
Hydrogen	1	91		60
Carbon	6	0.91		11
Nitrogen	7	0.42		2.4
Oxygen	8	0.057	62.6	26
Sodium	11	0.00012	2.6	0.7
Magnesium	12	0.0023	1.8	0.01
Aluminum	13	0.00023	6.5	
Silicon	14	0.026	21.2	0.00091
Phosphorus	15	0.00034		0.13
Sulfur	16	0.0091		0.13
Chlorine	17	0.00044		0.033
Potassium	19	0.000018	1.4	0.037
Calcium	20	0.00017	1.9	0.22
Iron	26	0.047	1.9	0.00059

roundings present when life first originated is as yet only a matter of speculation.

Although living matter often contains traces of all the elements found in its surroundings, only some 20 elements have been demonstrated to be essential for life. For convenience they can be classified in three major categories according to their relative concentration in the cell (Table 4-2): major constituents, trace elements, and ultratrace elements.

Not all these elements have been shown to be required by all species. Some of them we know to be of universal importance (H, C, N, O, Na, Mg, P, S, Ca, K) whereas others have been shown to be required in a large number of species and hence are probably also of general importance (Fe, Cu, Mn, Zn). The universality of the remaining elements (B, Si, V, Co, Mo) has so far not been established.

The study of the essential ultratrace elements is a continuing problem: one can never be certain that a particular element is *not* required, for it is a very laborious and technically complicated process to prove that it *is* required. The procedure involves the use of ultrapure water, chemicals, and even glassware. Thus the nutritional necessity of some ultratrace elements was not suspected until their near absence in certain soils caused the appearance of diseases and abnormalities in plants or animals. The absence of copper from

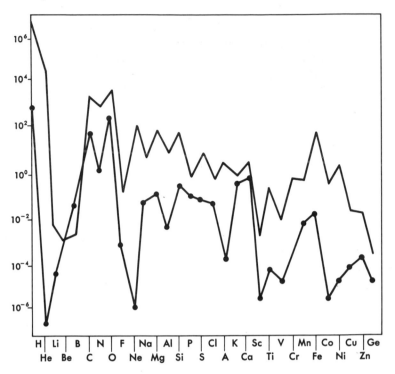

Fig. 4-1. Relative abundances of the first 31 elements in the cosmos (——, per 100 atoms Si) and in living organisms on the earth's surface (•——•, per 100 atoms C). (Courtesy of G. E. Hutchinson, 1943; uncorrected for recent data.)

certain regions in Australia caused a disease of sheep involving permanent effects on the nervous system, anemia, and deterioration of the wool with loss of kinkiness. A deficiency of boron in the soil has been observed to cause "heart rot" in beets, "cracked stems" in celery, "internal cork" in apples, and a host of other abnormalities in plants. The nutritional requirement of ultra-trace elements such as boron can best be shown by curing the deficiency disease through the addition of these elements to the soil. One hundredth of a part per billion of soil will cause the disease, one tenth of a part per billion will cure it, and one part per billion is a sufficiently high concentration to poison the plant.

What is the role of the 20-odd elements in the living machine? The elements H, C, N, O, P, and S are the building blocks of the cell's organic compounds. Most carbohydrates and lipids contain H, C, and O, while in addition proteins contain N and S, and nucleic acids N and P. Thus these six elements are the main constituents of the living machine. The ability of different permutations and combinations of these elements to produce the

TABLE 4-2

Elements Necessary for Life, and Some of Their Functions

Category	Element	Symbol	Atomic number	Some known functions
Major constituents 2–60 atoms percent	Hydrogen	H	1	Universally required for organic compounds of cell
	Carbon	C	6	
	Nitrogen	N	7	
	Oxygen	O	8	
Trace elements 0.02–0.1 atoms percent	Sodium	Na	11	Important counterion involved in action potential
	Magnesium	Mg	12	Cofactor of many enzymes
	Phosphorus	P	15	Universally involved in energy transfer reactions
	Sulfur	S	16	Found in proteins and other important substances
	Chlorine	Cl	17	One of major anions
	Potassium	K	19	Important counterion involved in nerve conduction, muscle contraction, etc.
	Calcium	Ca	20	Cofactor in enzymes, important constituent of membranes and regulator of membrane activity
Ultratrace elements less than 0.001 atoms percent	Boron	B	5	Important in plants, probably as cofactor of enzymes
	Silicon	Si	14	Found abundantly in many lower forms
	Vanadium	V	23	Found in certain pigments of lower forms
	Manganese	Mn	25	Cofactor of many enzymes
	Iron	Fe	26	Cofactor of many oxidative enzymes
	Cobalt	Co	27	Constituent of vitamin B_{12}
	Copper	Cu	29	Cofactor of many oxidative enzymes
	Zinc	Zn	30	Cofactor of many enzymes
	Molybdenum	Mo	42	Cofactor of a few enzymes

molecular diversity of the cell makes them unique in their fitness to support life. Cellular molecules range in nature from the gas carbon dioxide, through the liquid water, to the solid cellulose, and from the highly polar amino acid through the less polar glucose to the nonpolar fat. It has at times been suggested that on another planetary system silicon might replace carbon. This seems unlikely when one considers the full range of compounds and properties found in the world of carbon that could hardly be matched by a presumed world of silicon.

Many of the elements are usually found as ions; thus, Na^+, Mg^{2+}, PO_4^{2-}, SO_4^{2-}, Cl^-, K^+, and Ca^{2+}, and from the major elements, CO_3^{2-}, and NO_3^-. The importance of these ions to the well-being of the cell has been recognized for a long time. Thus the physiological literature of the twenties and thirties is replete with observations on the effect of ions such as Na^+, Mg^{2+}, K^+, and Ca^{2+} on the physical consistency and the functioning of a large variety of cells. The absolute amounts and the relative balance of these ions are maintained in living systems within narrow limits, and any experimental variation of these quantities results in marked changes in biological properties such as cellular permeability, irritability, contractility, protoplasmic viscosity, and cell division. The importance of the balance between these cations can be understood by a consideration of the fact that pairs of these ions often have been observed to have antagonistic effects on each other. Thus K^+ is known to decrease protoplasmic viscosity and to cause muscle relaxation, while Ca^{2+} has been observed to cause gelation of the cellular protoplasm as well as to initiate muscle contraction.

The importance of the ionic composition and balance in living systems can also be illustrated by the remarkable degree of maintenance of this parameter throughout biological evolution. Table 4-3 gives the ionic composition of a number of organisms of different evolutionary types along with the ionic composition of sea water. A. B. Macallum was the first to conclude that the parallelism shown here meant that life originated in the sea, and that subsequent evolution did little to change the ionic balance. After 1 billion years of evolution on land, though our body fluids are less concentrated than sea water, we still carry the ionic balance of sea water in our cells and body fluids.

There is as yet very little detailed understanding on a molecular basis of the role of these ions. Both proteins and nucleic acids (which are the main macromolecular components of the cell) are negatively charged polyvalent ions, and require cations as counterions. Furthermore, special relationships have been shown to exist between certain macromolecules and specific cations. Thus the concentration of Mg^{2+} has been shown to affect the state of aggregation of the ribosomes, probably through its effect on the RNA constituents of these bodies. These little cytoplasmic organelles, which we shall discuss later, have been shown to break into two smaller components

TABLE 4-3

Ionic Composition of Sea Water and the Body Fluids of Several Species
(Upper numbers are expressed in millimolar (mM) per liter;
lower numbers are relative, expressed in terms of 100 units of Na^+)

	Na^+	K^+	Ca^{2+}	Mg^{2+}	Cl^-	SO_4^{2-}
VERTEBRATES						
Man	145	5.1	2.5	1.2	103	2.5
(mammal)	(100)	(3.5)	(1.7)	(.83)	(71)	(1.7)
Rat	145	6.2	3.1	1.6	116	
(mammal)	(100)	(4.2)	(2.1)	(1.1)	(80)	
Frog	103	2.5	2.0	1.2	74	
(amphibian)	(100)	(2.4)	(1.9)	(1.2)	(72)	
Lophius	228	6.4	2.3	3.7	164	
(fish)	(100)	(2.8)	(1.0)	(1.6)	(72)	
INVERTEBRATES						
Hydrophilus	119	13	1.1	20	40	0.14
(insect)	(100)	(11)	(.93)	(17)	(34)	(.13)
Lobster	465	8.6	10.5	4.8	498	10
(arthropod)	(100)	(1.9)	(2.3)	(1.0)	(110)	(2.2)
Venus	438	7.4	9.5	25	514	26
(mollusk)	(100)	(1.7)	(2.2)	(5.7)	(120)	(5.9)
Sea cucumber	420	9.7	9.3	50	487	30
(echinoderm)	(100)	(2.3)	(2.2)	(12)	(120)	(7.2)
Sea water	417	9.1	9.4	50	483	30
	(100)	(2.2)	(2.3)	(12)	(120)	(7.2)

when the Mg^{2+} concentration is lowered. Calcium is almost certainly a counterion for the phospholipid constituents of the cell's membrane systems, and the effect of Ca^{2+} on lowering the threshold of nerve excitability is an example of this. And finally, potassium has been shown to interact selectively with myosin, the contractile protein of muscle. These are but a few examples from a field of cell biology that has yet to be fully explored on the molecular level.

But what about the ultratrace elements? What conceivable role could an element play if it is present at a concentration of 10^{-8} M? The answer seems simple and clear. In all cases that have been examined in detail, these ions turned out to be necessary "cofactors" for certain biological enzymes. Since enzymes, because of their catalytic nature, are generally required only in very low concentrations, it follows that their cofactors are also required in

TABLE 4-4

Some Metal-Requiring Enzymatic Reactions

glucose + ATP	$\xrightarrow[\text{Mg}^{2+}]{\text{hexokinase}}$	glucose 6 P + ADP
tryptophan + H_2O	$\xrightarrow[\text{K}^+ \text{ or Rb}^+]{\text{tryptophanase}}$	indole + pyruvate + NH_3
soluble fibrin	$\xrightarrow[\text{Ca}^{2+}]{\text{fibrinase}}$	insoluble fibrin
arginine + H_2O	$\xrightarrow[\text{Co}^{2+} \text{ or Mn}^{2+} \text{ or Ni}^{2+}]{\text{arginase}}$	urea + 2,5-diaminovaleric acid
histidine	$\xrightarrow[\text{Fe}^{3+} \text{ or Al}^{3+}]{\text{histidine decarboxylase}}$	histamine + CO_2
catechol	$\xrightarrow[\text{Cu}^{2+}]{\text{phenol oxidase}}$	o-benzoquinone
lactic acid + DPN	$\xrightarrow[\text{Zn}^{2+}]{\text{lactic dehydrogenase}}$	pyruvic acid + DPNH
nitrate + TPNH + H^+	$\xrightarrow[\text{Mo}^{2+}]{\text{nitrate reductase}}$	nitrite + TPN^+ + H_2O

very low concentrations. A small percentage of the trace elements mentioned above are also involved in enzyme activation. Table 4-4 gives a few examples of reactions utilizing enzymes that require certain specific metallic cofactors.

Some of the metallic ions can be prevented from functioning by the presence of certain inhibitors. The four iron atoms of the protein hemoglobin are the site of the oxygen-carrying function of that molecule. Cyanide or carbon monoxide can preferentially bind with the iron and hence interfere with the protein's ability to carry oxygen. Such compounds are *poisons*, and even in very low concentrations are capable of causing the death of the cell.

We have seen that living matter selects from its environment some 20 specific elements with which to build its fabric. In the next four chapters we shall examine a number of molecules that are elaborated by the cell and that perform the most important functions of the machinery of life.

SUGGESTED READING LIST

EDSALL, J. T., and WYMAN, J., 1958. *Biophysical chemistry*. New York: Academic Press.

FOWLER, W. A., "The origin of the elements," *Scientific American*, September 1956.

HENDERSON, L. J., 1958. *The fitness of the environment*. Boston: Beacon Press.

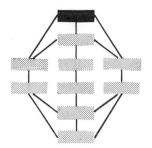

CHAPTER FIVE

WATER

AND

LIFE
Water is the dispersion medium of living matter. Even land organisms that at first glance would appear to thrive in a gaseous medium are found to live in a watery medium when examined at the cellular level. Actively living cells consist of 60 to 95 percent water, and the significance of water can be appreciated by the observation that even dormant cells and tissues like spores and seeds have water contents of 10 to 20 percent.

The ubiquity of water should not detract from its very special and unique properties. It is this uniqueness that makes water especially suited for the biological role it plays. The great physiologist L. J. Henderson once wrote a book entitled *The Fitness of the Environment,* in which he demonstrated that the phenomenon of biological adaptation could be considered not only from the point of view of organisms adapting to their environment, but also from the reverse direction—namely, from the point of view of the suitability of the physical environment for the support of life.

Water is a hydride of oxygen that possesses a uniquely strong degree of interaction between its molecules. Fig. 5-1 shows the heat of vaporization of a number of hydrides. The heat of vaporization is used here as a measure of the strength of intermolecular forces. We see that in the case of the carbon series there is a rough proportionality between the element forming the hydride and its heat of vaporization. This is not the case in the other series in which the first member is very atypical, with water being the most atypical of all. The reason for these unusually strong degrees of interaction is the fact that oxygen, fluorine, and nitrogen form hydrides in which only some of their electrons are involved in covalent bonds with the hydrogen while the remainder stay close to the atom, rendering it strongly electronegative. Thus these molecules have a high degree of electrical polarity, which in turn causes very strong intermolecular forces.

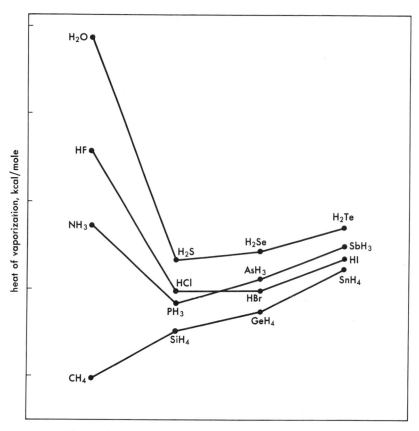

Fig. 5-1. Heats of vaporization of isoelectronic sequences of hydride molecules. (Courtesy of L. Pauling.)

Let us consider the case of the water molecule. The shape of this molecule is that of an isosceles triangle, with the hydrogens each sharing two electrons. The powerful attraction of the oxygen nucleus tends to draw the remaining four electrons away from the protons, thus leaving the region around them with a net positive charge. These two pairs of unshared electrons tend to concentrate in a region away from the hydrogen atoms, giving that region a negative charge. The geometry of this situation is such that if we consider the oxygen atom as the center of a tetrahedron, the two positive and the two negative centers of charge occupy the four corners of the tetrahedron. These centers of charge cause interactions, so that each molecule has an orienting effect on its four nearest neighbors. Thus two negative regions each attract a hydrogen (proton) of two other molecules and each proton attracts the oxygen of a neighbor. Each oxygen atom becomes, in this type of interaction, the center of a tetrahedron of other oxygens. There are, then, in water not only strong attractive forces but also a geometrical arrangement of these forces that lend themselves extremely well to the formation of three-dimensional structures. Fig. 5-2 is a representation of the arrangement of crystalline water. The linkages denoted by dotted lines are known as hydrogen bonds. These bonds also form when nitrogen and fluorine are substituted for oxygen, and this is why hydrogen fluoride and ammonia (see Fig. 5-1) are also endowed with very high heats of vaporization. But in the case of ammonia and hydrogen fluoride the geometry of interactions is such that only rings and chains are formed, thus making it impossible for them to form continuous, three-dimensional lattices. It follows that the properties of water are absolutely unique and it would seem unlikely that ammonia or hydrogen fluoride would be suitable as a dispersion medium for living systems in other planets.

This remarkable form of interaction of the hydrogen bond is stronger than the usual Van der Waal's forces, but weaker than the covalent bonds found in organic compounds. Its relative strength endows it with the ability to form structures and its relative weakness endows it with mobility. Without a doubt, the ability to form labile structures gives the hydrogen bond a

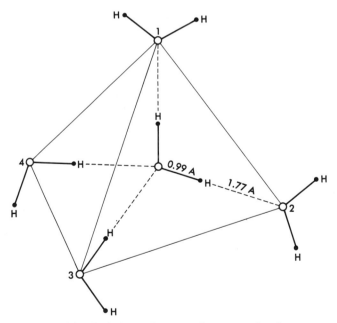

Fig. 5-2. Tetrahedral coordination of water molecules in ice. Molecules 1 and 2 as well as the central H_2O molecule lie entirely in the plane of the paper. Molecule 3 lies above this plane, and 4 below, so that oxygens 1, 2, 3, and 4 lie at the corners of a regular tetrahedron.

pre-eminent position in the behavior of living material, a fact to which we shall have ample opportunity to refer throughout this book.

The packing of water molecules in the ice crystal lattice is a *loose* one. When ice melts, this regular and loose arrangement changes into a more random, but more *compact* arrangement, causing an increase in density. Upon melting, the breakdown in structure is only partial, leaving a large portion of the liquid in a "paracrystalline" state, a unique and interesting property of water. As the temperature is slowly raised, more and more of the regular structure breaks down and the increase in density continues, reaching a maximum at 4°C. Thereafter, because of the effect of temperature on the increase in average distance between water molecules, the density of water decreases. This special property of water is responsible for the freezing of bodies of water from the top down, rather than the other way around. The layer of ice formed insulates the water below from heat loss, thus slowing down the freezing of lakes and rivers and protecting the life in them.

The structural features we have discussed so far are the cause of a number of other unique values for the melting point, boiling point, latent heat of fusion, heat capacity, surface tension, and dielectric constant. These properties each have important consequences for living matter.

There are three other aspects of the behavior of water that are of the most fundamental importance. First, water is an excellent solvent for many organic compounds. Because of the polarity of water and its hydrogen bonding capacity, it is able to dissolve organic compounds containing hydroxyl (—OH), carboxyl (—COOH), amino (—CNH$_2$), and keto (C=O) groups. At the same time it is also capable of dissolving salts that are completely dissociated into ions. Thus water has a uniquely broad spectrum of solvent action.

Second, water is itself capable of a slight degree of dissociation in the following manner:

$$O\text{—}H\text{---}\overset{\displaystyle\overset{H}{\diagup}}{O}\diagdown_{H} \quad \rightleftarrows \quad H\text{—}O^-\text{-----}H^{\pm}\overset{\displaystyle\overset{H}{\diagup}}{O}\diagdown_{H}$$

The equilibrium constant (K_w) of this reaction is 10^{-14}, which means that a kilogram of water contains only 10^{-7} moles of H_3O^+ ions (usually written as H^+), and $10^{-7}OH^-$ ions.

Third, water promotes the dissociation of a number of substances called "weak electrolytes." If such a substance gives off a proton (H^+), it is called a weak acid. The carboxyl and amino groups are the most frequently encountered weak electrolytes of the organic compounds of the cell (see Chapter 6).

It is possible to derive a simple equation relating the acidity (pH or negative logarithm of the proton or hydrogen ion concentration) to the pK (or the negative logarithm of the equilibrium constant) and the ratio of base to acid concentrations.

$$pH = pK + \log \frac{[\text{base}]}{[\text{acid}]}$$

This equation is extremely useful. For instance, it can be seen that when the concentrations of base and acid are equal, then the pH of a solution of a weak electrolyte is equal to its pK (since the logarithm of 1 is equal to 0). At that point the buffering capacity of the system—that is, its resistance to change in pH when protons are either added or withdrawn—is at a maximum. Another way of expressing this is to say that at a pH value numerically equal to its pK value, half of the acid is dissociated into its conjugate base.

As we shall see in succeeding chapters, the macromolecules, which are both the structural and functional entities of the cell, are weak polyelectrolytes that owe their state of dissociation, and hence many of their physical characteristics, to the presence of water or dilute salt solutions. Water, therefore, is not merely the dispersion medium of the cell but also a major influence on the properties of the molecules it disperses. The properties of water that we have discussed have innumerable connections with the functioning of the living machine. It is not any *one* but the simultaneous presence of all these properties that makes water the unique solvent for the world of life.

SUGGESTED READING LIST

Buswell, A. M., and Rodebush, W. H., "Water," *Scientific American*, April 1956.

Edsall, J. T., and Wyman, J., 1958. *Biophysical chemistry*. New York: Academic Press.

Henderson, L. J., 1958. *The fitness of the environment*. Boston: Beacon Press.

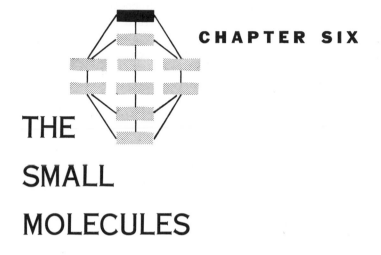

CHAPTER SIX

THE

SMALL

MOLECULES

OF THE

LIVING

MACHINE

MACHINE Organic chemistry, the chemistry of the living world, is the chemistry of carbon. An outstanding property of the carbon compounds utilized by the world of life is that they are remarkably inert, reacting only at infinitesimally low rates with each other, with water, and with atmospheric oxygen. This is so in spite of the fact that large amounts of energy are often released when these compounds do react. In Chapter 9 we shall discuss how the cell overcomes this sluggishness of organic compounds and utilizes it for purposes of molecular control. A second outstanding property of carbon is its versatility in forming a virtually unlimited number of compounds that vary widely in their properties. This inertness combined with versatility in the organic compounds of the cell are due to the following properties of carbon.

First, carbon is a light element with the atomic number 6. It shares, with other elements in the second horizontal row of the periodic table, the inability to expand its octet. Thus tetravalent carbon compounds are not complexed or solvated to any appreciable extent. Since reactions of other elements usually proceed via coordinated intermediates, it is not surprising that most reactions of carbon compounds are slow even though some of these reactions may involve the release of a great deal of energy.

Second, carbon, being centrally located in the periodic table, is capable of reacting both with electronegative elements like oxygen, nitrogen, phosphorus, sulfur, and chlorine as well as with the electropositive element hydrogen. Thus compounds of carbon are known in which formal oxidation states of −4, −2, 0, +2, and +4 can be assigned to the carbon atom. This ability to react with a variety of electropositive and electronegative elements is further expanded by the ability of carbon to form single, double, or triple

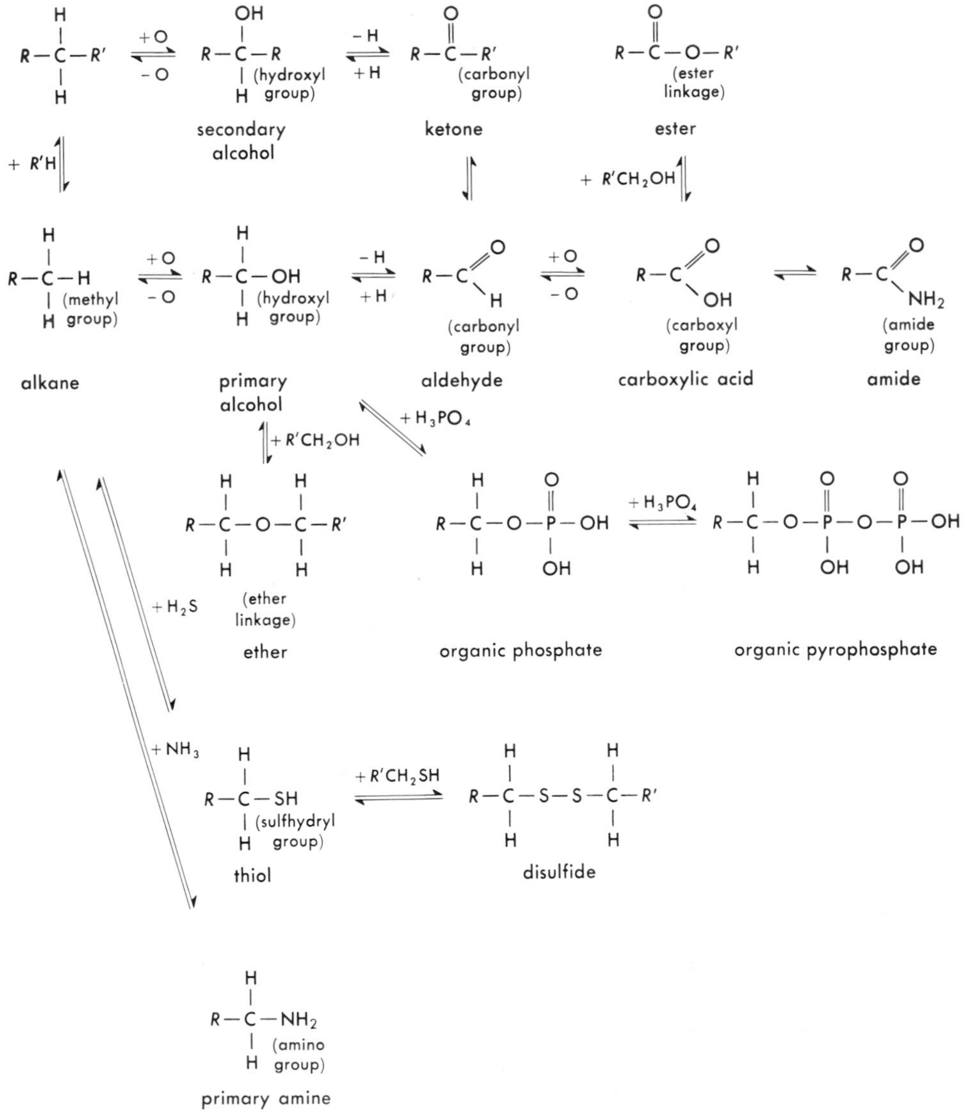

Fig. 6-1. Major aliphatic groups.

bonds **with** other carbon atoms. Since long carbon chains are stable, it is possible for carbon compounds to form straight or branched chains, rings, networks, and combinations of these structures.

The two sets of properties discussed above are shared separately by carbon with members of the same horizontal and vertical rows in the periodic table, respectively. Yet carbon is the only element that possesses *both* sets of properties, the slow reactivity and almost infinite versatility. One is forced to conclude that carbon is a truly unique element and that it is unlikely that a bios based on a different element would ever evolve in the universe.

We will discuss briefly the chemistry of the small organic molecules of the cell. Living material is a rich source of organic compounds that reflect the endless variability of microbial, plant, and animal species, but we shall restrict our attention to only a few of the most important compounds universally found in living matter.

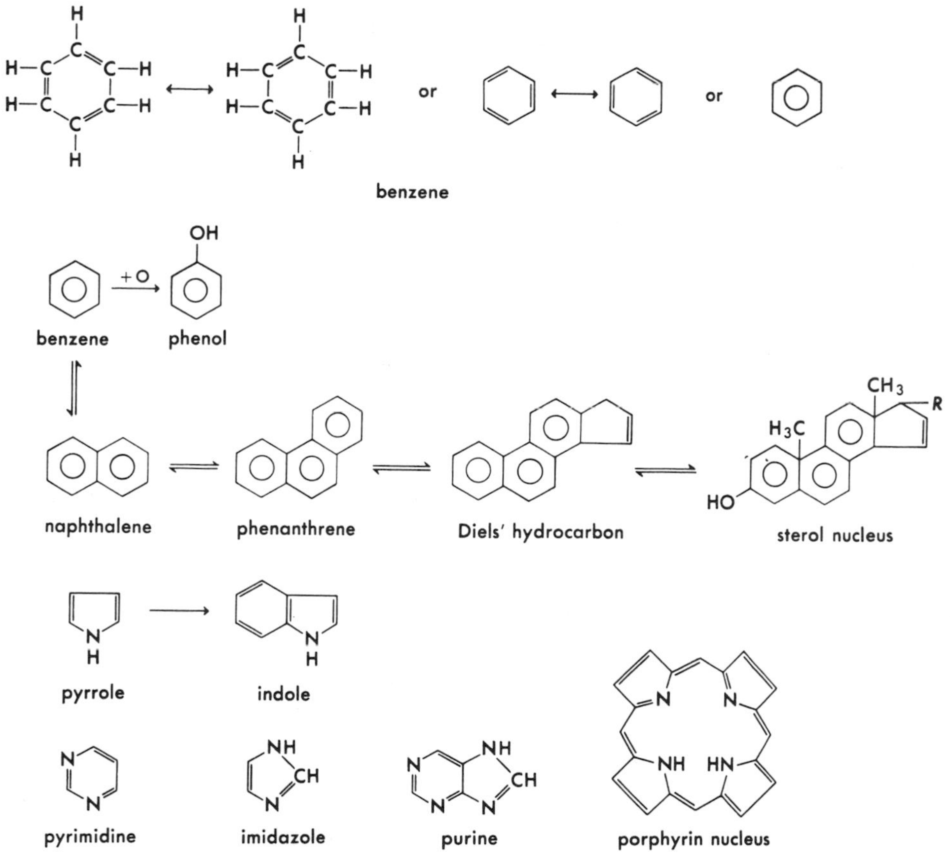

Fig. 6-2. Major aromatic groups.

CHEMICAL GROUPINGS

Figs. 6-1 and 6-2 (pp. 42 and 43) are flow sheets that relate the main organic groups found in living material. The carbohydrates, fats, nitrogen bases, amino acids, and other compounds are combinations of these groupings. The arrows in the flow sheets do not necessarily indicate pathways by which these compounds can best be synthesized but simply serve to indicate family relationships. The chemical and physical properties of each group are the subject matter of organic chemistry, and the student is referred to an elementary organic chemistry textbook for a detailed study.

Before beginning to list a number of biologically important structures we should mention a few phenomena that are important in the organic chemistry of living systems.

Dissociation

The main organic acids of the cell are the carboxylic acids and the organic phosphates.

carboxyl group $p\text{K}_{\text{COOH}} = 3\text{-}4$

organic phosphate $p\text{K}_1 = 2$ $p\text{K}_2 = 7$

The main organic bases of the cell are nitrogen-containing compounds.

$$R-NH_2 + H^+ \rightleftharpoons R-NH_3^+$$

amino group $p\text{K}_{\text{NH}_3^+} = 9\text{-}10$

imidazole group $p\text{K}_{\text{NH}^+} = 6\text{-}7$

guanidinium group $p\text{K}_{\text{NH}_2^+} = 12\text{-}13$

Solubility

Organic groups can be classified as *hydrophilic* if they promote solubility in aqueous solvents and *hydrophobic* if they promote solubility in the "nonpolar" (organic) solvents like benzene, toluene, etc. Hydrocarbon groups like $-CH_3$, $-C_2H_5$, and ⬡ are highly nonpolar and therefore hydrophobic, whereas dissociated groups like $-COO^-$, $-NH_3^+$ are highly polar and therefore hydrophilic. Between these two extremes lie a number of groups that endow their respective compounds with an intermediate solubility. The list below is a rough approximation, in ascending order, of the hydrophilic properties of a number of organic groupings.

Hydrogen Bonds

As we have already learned, hydrogen bonds are weak secondary valence forces between hydrogen and strongly electronegative atoms like F, O, or N.

tyrosyl   histidyl   seryl   aspartyl

The above examples of hydrogen bonds (dotted lines) will be encountered frequently in subsequent discussions. Hydrogen bond formation plays an important role in the solubility of organic compounds in aqueous solvents.

Optical Isomerism

When a carbon atom is bonded to four different groups there are two distinct spatial configurations possible and they are related to each other as an object is to its mirror image.

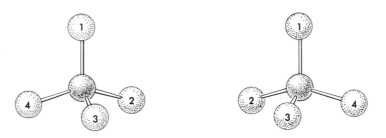

A solution of one member of a mirror image pair rotates the plane of *polarized light*. Its optical isomer will do the same but rotation is in the opposite direction.

Ultraviolet Light Absorption

A number of organic compounds of biological importance are colorless in visible light but absorb intensely in the near ultraviolet. This absorption is due to photons of the ultraviolet light exciting electrons in the molecule to higher energy levels, whereupon it is said to be in an "excited state." Such "excited state molecules" are usually so short lived that they cannot react chemically before losing their energy to surrounding molecules. However, in photosynthesis and other biologically important processes, energy from excited states is used to carry out important biochemical reactions.

The ease with which an electron in a particular molecule can be excited depends on the structure of that molecule. Compounds without double or triple bonds usually require considerable energy for electron excitation, and these absorb only in the far ultraviolet region where the wavelength is shorter and hence the energy higher. Compounds containing multiple bonds and particularly those in which two or more multiple bonds are adjacent absorb in the near ultraviolet or visible range. Biologically important examples of such molecules are the nitrogen bases of the nucleic acids (Chapter 7) and the amino acids tyrosine, tryptophan, and phenylalanine (Chapter 8). Ultraviolet absorption provides a convenient tool for measuring the concentration of these important compounds. Fortunately for the biologist, the absorption maximum for the nucleic acids is at 260 mμ and for these three amino acids at 280 mμ.

HIGH-ENERGY PHOSPHATE COMPOUNDS

The name high-energy phosphate was given to those phosphate esters whose hydrolysis leads to a uniquely high release of energy in the form of heat. Among these substances are some that will be mentioned later, such as adenosine triphosphate (ATP), the triphosphates of uridine, cytidine, and guanosine (UTP, CTP, GTP), phosphocreatine, phosphoenolpyruvic acid, amino acid adenylates, and uridine diphosphate glucose. For example, the hydrolysis of ATP leads to ΔH values (see Chapter 2) of about 9000 calories per mole, whereas other compounds, as glucose-6-phosphate, have ΔH values of about one-half of this. Actually, the high-energy content of the compound is more correctly given by the free energy of hydrolysis, the ΔF (see Chapter 2). The ΔF values are obtained from measurements of concentrations of the high-energy compounds in reactions in which they participate; they are a measure of differences between the free energies of reactants and of products. If the latter is higher, energy must be supplied for the reaction to proceed. The reasons for the "high-energy" nature of these compounds is not precisely known, but it is thought to be due to several factors that make these compounds unique: there are striking differences between the compounds and the products of their hydrolysis, as in their resonance stabilities, their ionizations, and the intramolecular electrostatic repulsions. It was noted by Lipmann and Kalckar, in 1941, that a prominent feature of the high-energy compounds is that they are anhydrides of phosphoric acid with a second acid, as a substituted phosphoric acid, to form the nucleoside di- and triphosphates; or with a carboxylic acid compound (acetic acid), to form acetyl phosphate; or even with an enol, to form phosphoenolpyruvic acid. In another case, however, phosphoric acid combines with a basic nitrogen compound, as in phosphocreatine. In all cases, the formation of the anhydride bond reduces the number of resonating groups in the molecule, and since the thermodynamic stability of a substance is increased by its ability to assume many resonating forms, the high-energy compounds are less stable and their hydrolysis will yield a large amount of heat. Fig. 6-3 shows some of these properties.

The most important high-energy compound is ATP. Its formula is shown in Fig. 6-4, and its modes of formation by the cell are given in Chapters 11 and 14. It can function in various ways: (1) as a phosphorylating agent, transferring inorganic phosphate to an acceptor compound, as in the hexokinase reaction to form glucose-6-phosphate (Fig. 10-1); (2) as a pyrophosphorylating agent, transferring inorganic pyrophosphate to an acceptor; or (3) as an adenylating agent, transferring the adenylate moiety to a suitable acceptor, as in the formation of the amino acid adenylates (Fig. 13-4). In all these cases the product synthesized can be at a lower, at the same, or

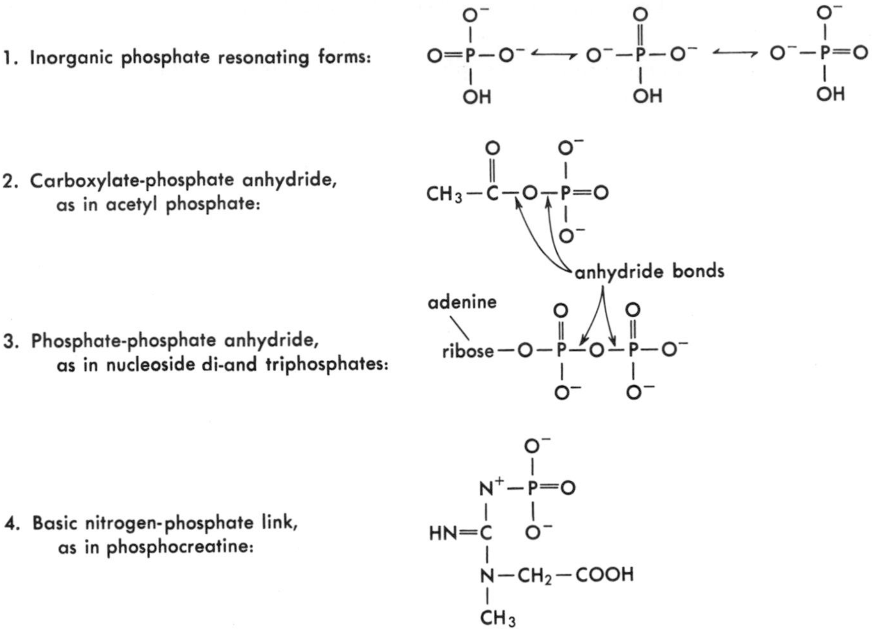

1. Inorganic phosphate resonating forms:

$$O{=}P{-}O^- \longleftrightarrow O^-{-}P{-}O^- \longleftrightarrow O^-{-}P{=}O$$

2. Carboxylate-phosphate anhydride, as in acetyl phosphate:

$$CH_3{-}C{-}O{-}P{=}O$$

anhydride bonds

3. Phosphate-phosphate anhydride, as in nucleoside di-and triphosphates:

adenine

ribose$-O-P-O-P-O^-$

4. Basic nitrogen-phosphate link, as in phosphocreatine:

$$N^+{-}P{=}O$$
$$HN{=}C \quad O^-$$
$$N{-}CH_2{-}COOH$$
$$CH_3$$

Fig. 6-3. Properties of "high-energy" compounds.

even at a higher energy level than is ATP. In the cell, ATP functions mostly as a phosphorylating agent, in those cases where energy is required to drive a reaction. ATP acts as a messenger between those reactions that supply energy (exergonic) and those that utilize energy (endergonic); it does so because it is common to both types of reactions.

Similarly, the other nucleoside diphosphates, guanylic, cytidylic, and uridylic, can be phosphorylated by ATP to give the corresponding triphosphates. These reactions are important in that all the nucleoside triphosphates are instrumental in synthetic reactions. ATP is involved in fatty acid and protein synthesis (see Chapter 13), CTP in phospholipid synthesis, UTP in glycogen synthesis (see Chapter 14), and GTP in carbohydrate and protein synthesis. The ultimate energy requirement for the synthetic needs of the cell is ATP, since only it is formed in glycolytic (see Chapter 14), photosynthetic, and oxidative phosphorylations (see Chapter 11). But from ATP the energy is funneled by countless transphosphorylation reactions to other "energy-donating" compounds. For example, glycogen is made from UDPG, a compound synthesized by the reaction of UTP with glucose-1-phosphate; the UTP is formed from ATP through the reaction ATP + UDP $\rightleftharpoons$ ADP + UTP. In addition, ATP can phosphorylate creatine, forming the phosphocreatine utilized by muscle fibrils (see Chapter 14). It can also phosphorylate acetate, giving acetyl phosphate, or it can transfer its adenylate moiety to acetate, forming acetyl adenylate. Both these compounds can be transformed into acetyl coenzyme A, which is the immediate precursor of fatty acids. The interconversions between the various classes of phosphorus compounds are given in Fig. 6-5. The problem presented by such a tabulation is how the cell can regulate, through the shunting of the high-energy groupings, the innumerable synthetic reactions that occur therein. In some cases, since the energy state of the phosphorylated acceptor compound is the same as or lower than that of ATP, it would appear that the availability of the acceptor compound, be it UDP or glucose, is used as a regulatory device. In other instances, as in the case of phosphocreatine or acetyl adenylate, the energy content is higher than that of ATP; hence the reaction would not go in the direction of synthesis of the phosphorylated acceptor compound, unless the concentration of the latter compound is reduced by being employed in yet another reaction, that of synthesis. In this way, the energy is used in the synthetic reaction, phosphate

Fig. 6-4. Chemical formula of ATP.

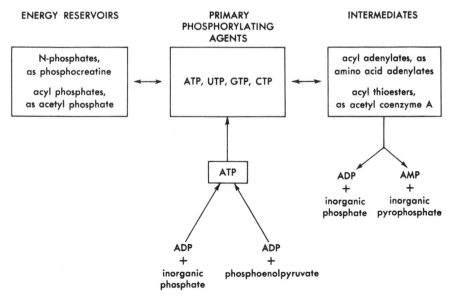

N-phosphates, as phosphocreatine acyl phosphates, as acetyl phosphate	ATP, UTP, GTP, CTP	acyl adenylates, as amino acid adenylates acyl thioesters, as acetyl coenzyme A

ATP

ADP + inorganic phosphate

ADP + phosphoenolpyruvate

ADP + inorganic phosphate

AMP + inorganic pyrophosphate

Fig. 6-5.   Interrelationships between "high-energy" compounds.

or pyrophosphate is split off, and thus the over-all reaction, starting from ATP, will be in the direction of synthesis of the phosphorylated intermediate, and hence synthesis of glycogen or protein or whatever else the case may be.

ORGANIC STRUCTURES

The organic compounds of the cell are often classified into the five categories of carbohydrates, lipids, proteins, nucleic acids, and "others." We shall restrict ourselves in this chapter to examples from the first and second categories.

Carbohydrates

Carbohydrates are a group of compounds characterized by having the general formula $(CH_2O)_n$.

D-*glucose*, a hexose, is the living world's most widespread 6-carbon sugar. It contains five hydroxyl groups and one aldehyde group. In solution it is found mostly in the form of a 6-membered ring that is in equilibrium with a small amount of the open-chain form. The ring (pyranose) form causes the aldehyde group to be relatively unreactive.

open-chain form   6-membered ring form   short representation

D - g l u c o s e

Since glucose has four asymmetric carbon atoms it has 16 isomers, but only three are found in nature. Because of the abundance of hydrogen-bonding hydroxyl groups, glucose is very soluble in water.

D-*ribose* is a 5-carbon sugar (pentose), which we shall see is extremely important in the chemistry of heredity (since it is a component of DNA and RNA) and in the metabolism of energy transfer (since it is a part of ATP). Its derivative is deoxyribose.

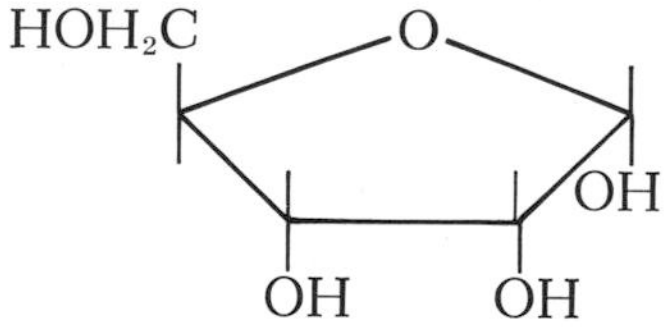

$$HOH_2C \qquad O$$

OH   OH

D-ribose

D-*glyceraldehyde* is an important intermediate in the anaerobic metabolism of carbohydrate (see Chapter 14).

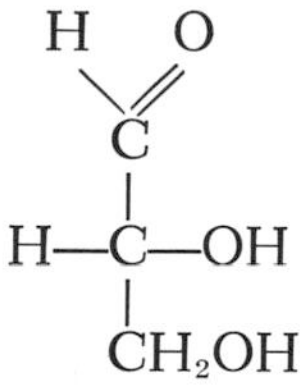

H   O

C

H—C—OH

CH_2OH

D-glyceraldehyde

Hexoses and pentoses can *polymerize* into straight and branched chains of variable lengths to form polysaccharides, which are structural materials like cellulose or storage products like starch (in plants) or glycogen (in animals).

Lipids

Lipids are not necessarily related in chemical structure since they are defined by the common physical property of solubility in nonpolar, organic solvents.

Fatty acids of the "saturated" variety have the general formula

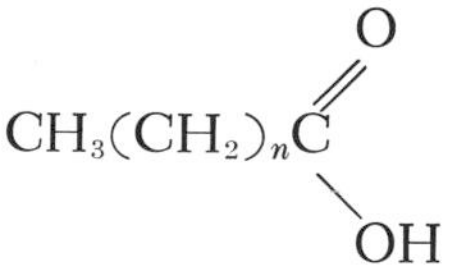

$$O$$
$$CH_3(CH_2)_nC$$
$$OH$$

A typical example is palmitic acid

$$CH_3(CH_2)_{14}COOH$$

Unsaturated fatty acids have one or more double bonds. For example, oleic acid, which has only one such bond, has the following formula

$$CH_3(CH_2)_7CH=CH(CH_2)_7COOH$$

Fatty acids have the special property of being composed of a very nonpolar, hydrophobic hydrocarbon chain and a very polar, dissociating carboxyl group. This causes the fatty acid to form an oriented, monomolecular layer at a water interface, an effect that lowers considerably the surface tension of water.

This explains the cleaning power of *soaps* that are sodium or potassium salts of fatty acids.

Fats are esters of glycerol and fatty acids.

$$
\begin{array}{ccc}
\text{CH}_2\text{O}{\mid}\text{H} & \text{HO}{\mid}\text{OC(CH}_2)_n\ \text{CH}_3 & \\
| & & \\
\text{CHO}{\mid}\text{H} & + \quad \text{HO}{\mid}\text{OC(CH}_2)_{n'}\ \text{CH}_3 & \rightleftharpoons \\
| & & \\
\text{CH}_2\text{O}{\mid}\text{H} & \text{HO}{\mid}\text{OC(CH}_2)_{n''}\text{CH}_3 & \\
\text{glycerol} & \text{fatty acids} &
\end{array}
$$

$$
\begin{array}{c}
\ \ \ \ \text{H} \quad\quad\ \text{O} \\
\ \ \ \ | \quad\quad\ \ \| \\
\text{H}-\text{C}-\text{O}-\text{C}-(\text{CH}_2)_n\ \text{CH}_3 \\
| \\
\ \ \ \ \ \ \ \ \ \ \text{O} \\
\ \ \ \ \ \ \ \ \ \ \| \\
\text{H}-\text{C}-\text{O}-\text{C}-(\text{CH}_2)_{n'}\text{CH}_3 \\
| \\
\ \ \ \ \ \ \ \ \ \ \text{O} \\
\ \ \ \ \ \ \ \ \ \ \| \\
\text{H}-\text{C}-\text{O}-\text{C}-(\text{CH}_2)_{n''}\text{CH}_3 \\
| \\
\text{H} \\
\text{fat}
\end{array}
$$

Because the polar carboxyl groups are tied up in fats in the form of the far less polar ester linkages, fats are highly insoluble in water.

Phospholipids are esters of glycerol and one or two fatty acids containing in addition some nitrogen and phosphorus compounds.

$$
\begin{array}{c}
\ \ \ \ \ \ \ \ \ \ \text{H} \quad\quad\ \text{O} \\
\ \ \ \ \ \ \ \ \ \ | \quad\quad\ \ \| \\
\ \ \ \ \ \ \ \ \text{H}-\text{C}-\text{O}-\text{C}-R \\
\ \ \ \ \text{O} \quad\quad | \\
\ \ \ \ \| \quad\quad\quad | \\
R-\text{C}-\text{O}-\text{C}-\text{H} \\
\ \ \ \ \ \ \ \ \ \ \ \ | \quad\quad\ \ \text{O}^- \quad\ \text{N}^+(\text{CH}_3)_3 \\
\ \ \ \ \ \ \ \ \ \ \ \ | \quad\quad\ \ | \quad\quad\ \ | \\
\ \ \ \ \ \ \text{H}-\text{C}-\text{O}-\text{P}{=}\text{O} \quad \text{CH}_2 \\
\ \ \ \ \ \ \ \ \ \ | \quad\quad\ \ | \quad\quad\ \ | \\
\ \ \ \ \ \ \ \ \ \ \text{H} \quad\quad\ \text{O}{-}{-}{-}\text{CH}_2 \\
\text{lecithin}
\end{array}
$$

The formula is that of a lecithin that contains phosphoric acid and a nitrogen base called *choline*. Because of the two charges at one end and the nonpolar characteristics of the other end, phospholipids tend to be very surface active. In the cell they are found as a structural component of the semipermeable membranes.

Steroids are lipids derived from a phenanthrene structure and hence very different in their chemical constitution from fatty acids, fats, and phospholipids. Steroids are found as structural components of the membranes and also as *hormones*, and as such play an important role in the physiological regulation of animal metabolism.

cholesterol

Cholesterol is a well-known, widely distributed steroid.

The *nitrogen bases* and the *amino acids* are the building blocks of the nucleic acids and proteins respectively and will therefore be treated in the next two chapters. Other compounds, such as organic acids, phosphorylated intermediates, etc., will be discussed in Chapters 10 and 11.

We have discussed here the more important small molecules of the cell. We shall learn later about the role these molecules play in the "metabolic flux" that is so characteristic of the world of life.

As we have seen in Chapter 3, the cell is not a droplet of liquid containing a mixture of small molecules in solution. It is, rather, matter in a *colloidal state of aggregation,* possessing both the elastic properties of a solid and the viscous properties of a liquid. Furthermore, the cell is not made of one "protoplasmic" material but of a number of distinct organelles suspended in a ground substance that is interlaced by a hydrophobic network of membranes. Clearly the cell has an intricate fine structure within which the metabolic flux of the small molecules is delicately regulated. The building blocks giving rise to this fine structure are the macromolecules of the cell, the nucleic acids and the proteins. It is therefore important, in order to understand the structure and function of the cellular organelles, to study in some detail the structural chemistry of the cellular macromolecules.

SUGGESTED READING LIST

BALDWIN, E., 1957. *Dynamic aspects of biochemistry*, 3d ed. Cambridge: Cambridge University Press.

FRUTON, J. S., and SIMMONDS, S., 1958. *General biochemistry*, 2d ed. New York: Wiley.

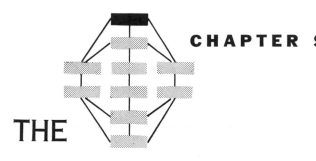

CHAPTER SEVEN

THE

NUCLEIC ACIDS,

CARRIERS OF

BIOLOGICAL

INFORMATION

The history of science is often pictured as a one-way process of constantly widening and deepening insight into the unity of nature. But science is also a human activity, and its progress reveals much about the mind and spirit of man. It illustrates his capability to divest himself of prejudice, his readiness to accept the loneliness that comes through a detachment from the mainstream of human thought, his ability to communicate productively with his fellows across national and even ideological boundaries. This humanistic meaning of science can best be grasped when we examine the lives of some of its most outstanding practitioners. Such a man was Friedrich Miescher (1844–1895) who anticipated an approach to the biology of the cell that has come into its own only during the last twenty years. In 1868 Miescher set himself the task of studying the chemistry of the nucleus. At that time the significance of the nucleus was barely understood, for it was only in 1876 that Oskar Hertwig was able to demonstrate that fertilization of the sea urchin egg involved the fusion of two nuclei, one from the egg, and one from the sperm. It had been previously pointed out by a number of thinkers including Leonardo da Vinci (1452–1519) that since the hereditary result of a given mating was unaffected by the direction in which the cross was made, both male and female must contribute equally to the heredity of the offspring. Miescher must have been aware of this as well as of the fact that sperm consists of little else than nuclear material. He thus must have surmised, even before Hertwig's observations of nuclear fusion, that the nucleus is the repository of hereditary information. Armed with this brilliant and prophetic insight, Miescher approached his problem in a manner that was half a century ahead of his contemporaries. To begin with, he assumed that the biological phenomenon of heredity must have a chemical basis. Second, he chose a biological material well suited for the isolation of nuclei: the pus cells obtained from the discarded bandages of wounded soldiers, made abundantly available by the Franco-Prussian War. Third, he used an amazingly modern technique to delicately rupture his cells: digestion with pepsin-hydrochloric acid, followed by ether extraction that layered his intact nuclei at the bottom of the test tube. Thus, without the aid of differential centrifugation, Miescher was able to isolate for the first time a cellular organelle. By treating the nuclei with a salt solution followed by acidification, Miescher obtained a material that had a property hitherto observed only in some lipid fractions: it contained large amounts of phosphorus. Miescher called this material *nuclein*. It was later renamed *deoxyribonucleic acid* (DNA) and is now recognized as being the chemical structure that stores the cell's hereditary information.

Miescher followed his discovery with many years of careful experimentation. By fractionating the sperm heads of the Rhine salmon at low temperature, he was able to show that the nuclein was a material of high molecular weight and that it was associated with an unusually basic protein which he called *protamine*. His measurement of the phosphorus content of "nuclein" (9.95 percent) corresponds with our modern values for DNA (9.22 to 9.24 percent) and is a tribute to the excellence of his preparations. When Miescher died he left to his student Altmann the firm foundations of an entirely new field in biology, which he, a single individual, had initiated. Thus our understanding of the molecular basis of heredity was born just at the time when Mendel was discovering some of its biological manifestations.

THE ORGANIC CHEMISTRY OF THE NUCLEIC ACIDS

The forty years following Miescher's death saw the elucidation of the organic chemistry of the nucleic acids. It became apparent that there were two classes of these acids. Deoxyribonucleic acid (DNA) was found to be composed of (1) the purine nitrogen bases *adenine* and *guanine*, (2) the pyrimidine nitrogen bases *cytosine* and *thymine*, (3) the pentose sugar *deoxyribose*, and (4) *phosphoric acid* (Fig. 7-1). *Ribonucleic acid* (RNA) was found to be composed of the same building blocks except that the pyrimidine *uracil* is substituted for *thymine* and the pentose *ribose* for *deoxyribose* (Fig. 7-1).

In the last twenty years, with the help of special enzymes called

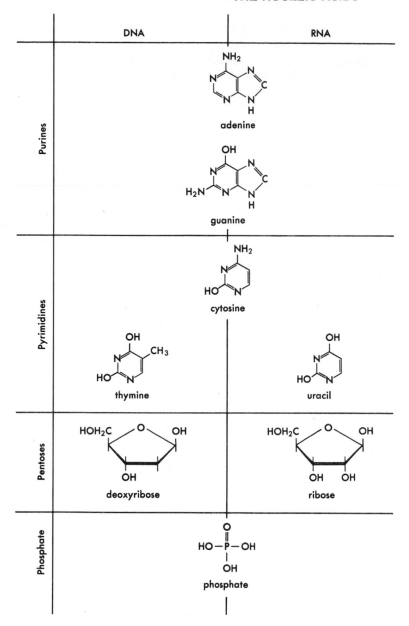

Fig. 7-1.   The building blocks of DNA and RNA.

nucleases, which have the ability to split either DNA or RNA at various specific points in their macromolecular structure, it has been possible to find out how these building blocks of DNA and RNA are arranged inside the molecule. In both DNA and RNA the purine and pyrimidine nitrogen bases are linked to the dexoxyribose or ribose respectively to form *nucleosides* (Fig. 7-2), whereas phosphate is attached to the sugars to form *nucleotides* (Fig. 7-2).

How then are the nucleotides tied together in the polymer? We now know from a number of separate lines of evidence that both DNA and RNA are linear, unbranched polymers of nucleosides linked together by phosphate groups. The nitrogen bases, as we have already shown in Fig. 7-2, are attached to the pentose units. Fig. 7-3 represents sample chains or "polynucleotides" of the DNA and RNA type.

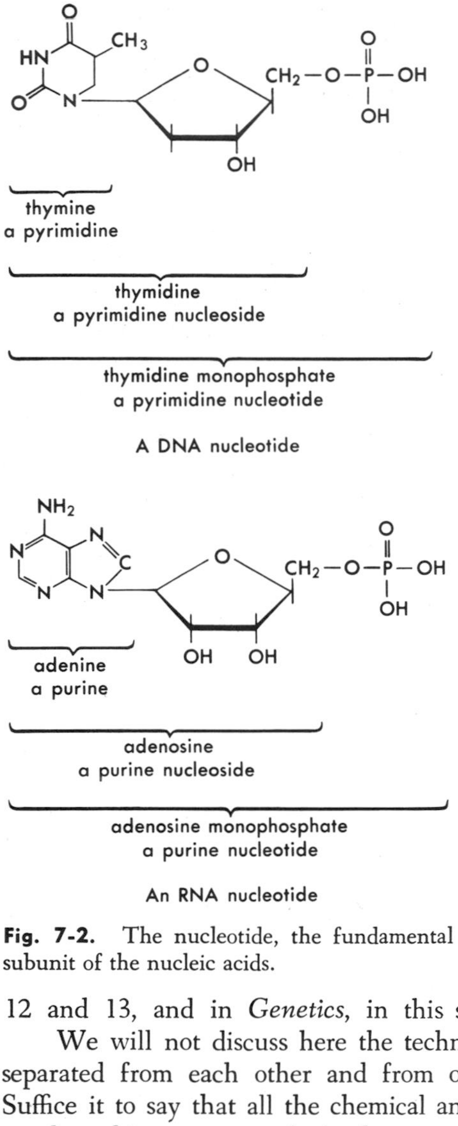

thymine
a pyrimidine

thymidine
a pyrimidine nucleoside

thymidine monophosphate
a pyrimidine nucleotide

A DNA nucleotide

adenine
a purine

adenosine
a purine nucleoside

adenosine monophosphate
a purine nucleotide

An RNA nucleotide

Fig. 7-2. The nucleotide, the fundamental subunit of the nucleic acids.

INDICATIONS OF BIOLOGICAL FUNCTION

While these painstaking investigations on the organic chemistry of the nucleic acids were in progress, a number of important developments led to a clarification of their biological function. The more recent developments in this field are discussed in Chapters 12 and 13, and in *Genetics*, in this series.

We will not discuss here the techniques whereby DNA and RNA are separated from each other and from other cell constituents like proteins. Suffice it to say that all the chemical and biological discoveries rest squarely on the achievements made in the area of purification. Of equal importance were the discoveries that DNA reacts with Schiff's reagent to give a brilliant purple color (the Feulgen reaction), that both DNA and RNA react with basic dyes, and that DNA and RNA absorb ultraviolet light with great in-

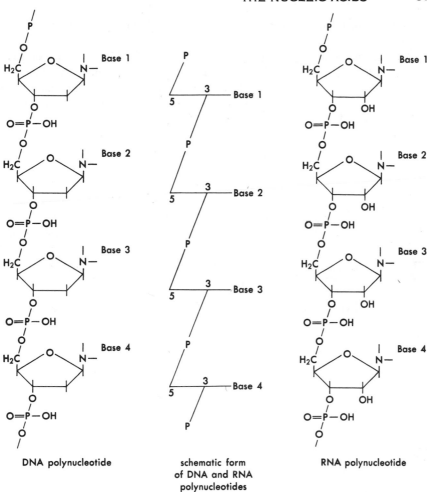

Fig. 7-3. The structure of DNA and RNA polynucleotides.

tensity in the 240 to 280 mμ region with an absorption maximum at about 260 mμ (Fig. 7-4). In analyzing these discoveries a large number of ingenious methods were developed to localize the DNA and RNA in the cell. Caspersson developed ultraviolet microscopes, microspectrophotometers, and various microchemical methods designed to estimate the nucleic acid content of cell particulates. From these studies we have learned (1) that DNA is localized primarily on the chromosomes, although there are a few reports of DNA in chloroplasts and even in the cytoplasm of eggs, (2) that the bulk of the RNA is found in the cytoplasm, and (3) that of the small amount of RNA found in the nucleus some is located in the nucleolus and the rest is associated with the chromosomes or is found freely in the nuclear sap. As we shall see in Chapter 13, the bulk of the cytoplasmic RNA is located in the ribosomes.

By far the most significant experiments on the biological role of the nucleic acids were performed with microorganisms. Since these experiments are discussed in some detail in both *Genetics* and *Microbial Life,* in this series, we will simply list them here. (1) The isolation and purification of many viruses and the demonstration that these self-duplicating systems are deoxyribo- or ribonucleo-protein. (2) The work by Avery, MacLeod, and McCarty showing that DNA from the R (encapsulated) strain of pneumococcus could completely and permanently transform cells of the S (nonencapsulated) type into the R type. (3) The work of Hershey and Chase showing that during virus infection the DNA of the T_2 virus entered the bacterial cell while most of the protein of the virus remained outside. (4) The work by Fraenkel-Conrat and Schramm showing that for the RNA-carrying tobacco mosaic virus it was the RNA alone that determined the special characteristics of a given strain of virus.

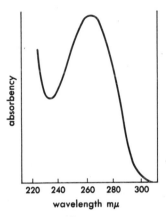

Fig. 7-4. Absorption spectrum of a nucleic acid.

Thus by the mid-fifties these and other experiments had led to the generally held belief that DNA is the hereditary material of the cell and that protein synthesis is in some way mediated by RNA. Since the gene must be the ultimate determinant of protein specificity, it was surmised that DNA and RNA metabolism were related. We shall discuss in Chapters 12 and 13 to what extent these predictions of the fifties have been proved essentially correct. Here, however, we shall examine in more detail the three-dimensional structure of the nucleic acids.

THE STRUCTURE OF DNA

We have learned so far that DNA and RNA are polynucleotides that form long unbranched chains. This information does not tell us, however, how these molecules are organized three-dimensionally. As we shall see again and again, the precise three-dimensional configuration of biological macromolecules is of prime importance to the understanding of their biological function, and it is in this area of cellular biology that some of the most exciting developments have taken place during the last decade.

In 1950 it was pointed out by Chargaff that in DNA the amount of adenine equals the amount of thymine and the amount of guanine equals the amount of cytosine. At the same time Wilkins and a number of other workers in England obtained some precise measurements on fibers "spun" from DNA, utilizing the x-ray diffraction method. This powerful method, which is playing an increasingly important role in molecular biology, uses the diffraction of x-ray beams for the detection of a periodic or repeating pattern in molecular or crystal structure. Measurements of DNA showed that there is a repeating pattern at intervals of 28 to 34 A. These dimensions were especially intriguing since nothing in the chemical structure along the length of the linear polymer appeared to correspond with these dimensions: the distance from one phosphate to the next is only about 7 A.

Physical measurements on DNA solutions of such properties as viscosity and light scattering indicated that the DNA molecule is very large (molecular weights of 10^5 to 10^7) and has the shape of very long, relatively stiff rods.

Watson and Crick, while collaborating at the Cavendish Laboratory in Cambridge, England, proposed in 1953 a structure for DNA that satisfied the above observations. Using known information about bond distances and bond angles in organic molecules, they built a scale model of the DNA molecule. It occurred to them that the 28 to 34 A repeat pattern might be satisfied by a helix. That in fact the molecule was a *double* helix of two separate strands of DNA twisted around each other must have suggested itself to them when they considered the A = T, G = C complementarity discovered by Chargaff. The double-stranded helix scale model that emerged proved to have interesting properties.

First, Watson and Crick pointed out that in order to have maximum symmetry the two strands must run in opposite directions. Note by referring back to Fig. 7-3 that the strands of DNA, irrespective of the order of the bases, are not the same if read from the left and from the right.

Second, they found that the double-stranded structure is stabilized by the nitrogen bases, which point toward each other and are capable of forming hydrogen bonds. It turned out that these bridges that hold together the

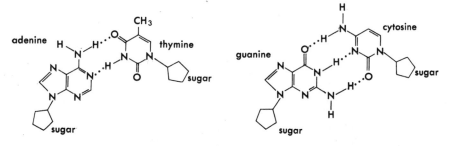

Fig. 7-5. Hydrogen bonding between adenine-thymine and guanine-cytosine.

two strands of the double helix can only be formed
between purines and pyrimidines, since there is
not enough room for two purines and too much
room for two pyrimidines. Furthermore, as can
be observed from Fig. 7-5, the only purine and
pyrimidine pairs capable of forming hydrogen
bonds are adenine-thymine (two hydrogen bonds)
and guanine-cytosine (three hydrogen bonds).
This conclusion has since been supported by an
overwhelming body of stereochemical and other
evidence, and is one of the most exciting in the
history of biology. Thus the $A = T$, $C = G$ equality suggests a double helix; a double helix is
constructed and one finds that it has the stereochemical properties of uniquely determining the
$A = T$, $C = G$ equality.

Third, it became clear that the nature of the
model placed no restrictions on the sequence in
which the base pairs follow each other. Thus it
appears that different DNA molecules are identical
in their gross architecture, differing only in the
specific sequence of their base pairs.

Fig. 7-6 shows two models of the Watson-
Crick DNA double helix. The first illustrates the
now famous basic geometric pattern of a "twisted
rope ladder with solid rungs," and shows the
positioning of the constituent building blocks,
the phosphates, the sugars, and the bases held in pairs by hydrogen bonds.
The second model utilizes the proper atomic volumes and illustrates the
amount of space occupied by the various groupings.

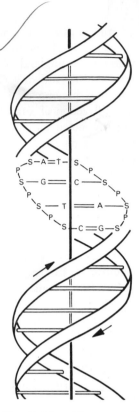

Fig. 7-6A. Diagrammatic
model of a small portion of
the DNA molecule.

Much evidence has been collected in recent years to make the Watson-
Crick hypothesis one of the most firmly entrenched generalizations of biological theory. This evidence includes (1) further and more extensive x-ray
diffraction studies; (2) direct visualization with the electron microscope
(Fig. 7-7), which showed that the mass per unit length is in agreement with
the model; (3) physical-chemical data on the so-called "melting point" of
DNA, which is the temperature at which the hydrogen bonds break co-
operatively, causing the stiff DNA molecules to collapse; (4) enzymatic
digestion studies in which the kinetics observed follow a pattern predicted
from a double-stranded structure, and finally (5) the spectacular work of
Kornberg and his group in accomplishing the synthesis of DNA in the test
tube (see Chapter 12).

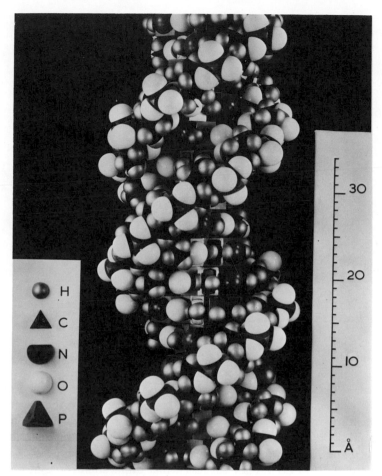

Fig. 7-6B. Scale atomic model of the DNA molecule. (Courtesy of M. H. F. Wilkins, King's College, England.)

Biological Significance

It has long been suggested that the genetic or hereditary material of the cell must have two separate functions. It must be capable of self-duplication and of initiating actions that ultimately find expression in a given cell structure or function. As a result of the work in biochemical genetics started by Ephrussi and by Beadle and Tatum (see *Genetics*, in this series) it now appears that the expression of gene action is the formation of a protein, be it an enzyme or a structural protein. DNA must therefore be capable both of duplicating itself and of providing the necessary information for protein

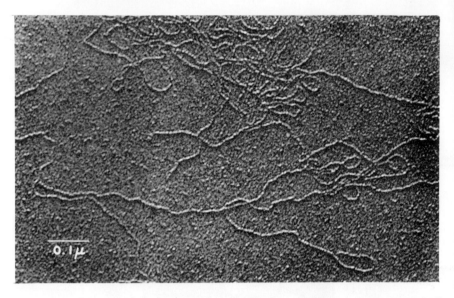

Fig. 7-7.   DNA molecules from salmon sperm ($\times$ 108,150). (Courtesy of C. E. Hall and M. Litt, Massachusetts Institute of Technology.)

synthesis. It is obvious that the structure of DNA provides a convenient device whereby a particular molecule with a particular sequence of base pairs could be duplicated. Thus each strand of the molecule could determine the laying down of a "complementary strand," resulting in the formation of two identical molecules (Fig. 7-8A). A precise geometrical model whereby the duplication of a DNA molecule could occur in a continuous manner without requiring the prior separation of strands was suggested by Levinthal and Crane (Fig. 7-8B). They suggested that duplication could begin at one end, thus opening up the strand and providing the energy for the rotation of the two lengthening daughter strands as well as the shortening parent strand. They concluded that enough energy was available to overcome the viscous drag opposing these rotations and that there was enough mechanical strength in the helix to withstand the necessary torque without seriously stretching the bonds. The duplicating DNA helix shown in Fig. 7-8B is now a familiar symbol of the science of molecular biology.

As for the role of DNA in storing and transmitting information to be used in protein synthesis, it would appear that the specific sequence of the bases along this linear structure provides the code necessary for the determination of protein structure. In a later chapter we will elaborate further on this crucial function of the cell. Suffice it here to point out Crick's suggestion that, if one were to imagine the pairs of bases corresponding to the dots and dashes of the Morse code, there is enough DNA in the human cell to encode

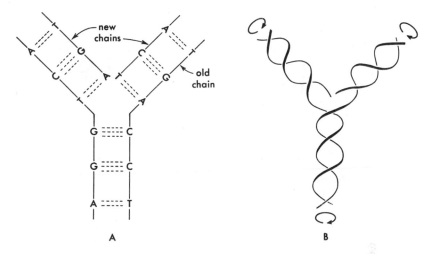

Fig. 7-8.   The replication of the DNA molecule.

1000 large textbooks. We have suggested in an earlier chapter that a signal characteristic of the living machine is its capability for "microminiaturization." Here indeed is a striking example of this cellular property: the ability of 20×10^{-12}g of DNA in the human fertilized egg to determine all the hereditary characteristics of the mature human individual weighing 5×10^{15} as much. Or, as has been often stated, all the DNA determining the hereditary characteristics of the entire population of the earth could be packed into the head of a pin.

THE STRUCTURE OF RNA

Our understanding of the structure and biological function of RNA is more recent in origin and less complete than that of DNA. There is now evidence for at least three types of cellular RNA, not counting the RNA of plant and some animal viruses. We shall discuss the biological function of RNA in some detail in Chapters 12 and 13 and will therefore limit our present discussion to structural considerations.

About 60 to 80 percent of the cell's RNA is found in the ribosomal particles. These large ribonucleoprotein particles can be extracted to yield preparations of RNA of very high molecular weight (5×10^5 to 2×10^6).

Very recently a new form of RNA has been identified, which has been named *messenger RNA*. Currently it is thought to be manufactured in the nucleus and that after entering the cytoplasm it attaches itself to the ribosomes. This attachment appears to depend on the Mg^{2+} concentration, 10^{-2}M promoting attachment and 10^{-4}M promoting dissociation. Estimates of molec-

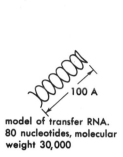

model of transfer RNA.
80 nucleotides, molecular
weight 30,000

Fig. 7-9. Double-helix models of single chains in transfer RNA (courtesy of M. H. F. Wilkins) and hypothetical structure of ribosomal RNA.

hypothetical structure for ribosomal RNA, showing helical and nonhelical regions

ular weight of messenger RNA so far indicate that it is a polydisperse material ranging in molecular weight from 5×10^4 to 5×10^5 and possibly even larger.

A third form of RNA, termed *transfer RNA*, is of low molecular weight (30,000), and for reasons that will become apparent later (Chapter 13), we expect some 20 different molecular species to occur in the cell, one for each amino acid found in proteins.

The structural organization of RNA has until recently been a complete mystery. In June of 1962 Wilkins and his collaborators reported that they had succeeded in crystallizing sodium salts of transfer RNA. X-ray crystallographic studies of these crystals reveal the same structural principles found in DNA; that is, a double helix made of antiparallel chains held together by hydrogen bonding between complementary bases. The difference in the RNA appears to be that the double helix is made of *one chain* folded in the middle and twisting around itself (see Fig. 7-9). They suggested that this leaves three unpaired bases at one end capable of hydrogen bonding with three bases possibly on the messenger RNA. The implications of this suggestion will become more apparent in Chapter 13.

Wilkins and his co-workers suggest that the other forms of RNA also contain extensive double-helix regions, as indeed is also suggested by a number of different physical-chemical studies. But since ribosomal RNA, unlike transfer RNA and messenger RNA, does not have A = T and G = C equality, only some portions of this RNA can be expected to be double helical (Fig. 7-9).

It is thought that the role of the RNA is to convert the message of the DNA into a form that can be utilized for protein synthesis, and we shall have more to say about this in Chapter 13. It is appropriate now, however, to consider the *proteins*, which are the physiologically active and structurally significant macromolecules of the cell.

SUGGESTED READING LIST

ALLEN, J. M., ed., 1962. *The molecular control of cellular activity.* New York: McGraw-Hill.

CHARGAFF, E., and DAVIDSON, J. N., eds., 1955. *The nucleic acids.* New York: Academic Press.

CRICK, F. H. C., "Nucleic acids," *Scientific American,* September 1957.

————, "The structure of the hereditary material," *Scientific American,* October 1954.

DAVIDSON, J. N., 1960. *The biochemistry of nucleic acids,* 4th ed. New York: Wiley.

KORNBERG, A., 1962. *Enzymatic synthesis of DNA.* New York: Wiley.

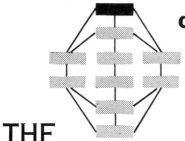

CHAPTER EIGHT

THE PROTEINS, AGENTS OF BIOLOGICAL SPECIFICITY

Proteins, as the derivation of the word implies, are of primary importance to the life of the cell. As Table 8-1 shows, proteins constitute the major component of the dry weight of an actively growing cell. What is so remarkable about proteins is that they are not only the main building material of the cell, but are also the regulators of all the activities carried out by the living machine. To perform their regulatory function, proteins are endowed with *specificity*, the ability to distinguish between different molecules. This property, more than any other, is characteristic of the phenomenon of life itself. This specificity of proteins is believed not only to permit the regulation of the multitude of cellular processes, but also to be the molecular basis of the differences that exist between individuals and between species.

An abiding law of nature is that structure and function are related. Thus we believe that the key to understanding how proteins behave is to know in detail how they are put together. In the last fifteen years an astounding series of developments have added to our knowledge of the structure of proteins. We shall attempt here to give an account of these developments in order to build in the mind of the student a vivid picture of the protein molecule.

TABLE 8-1

Typical Analytic Results Obtained upon Fractionation of Rapidly Growing Cells

(These results are characteristic for cells lacking polysaccharide cell walls or large amounts of other structural and storage materials)

Material	Criteria used for fraction	Percent dry weight
Small molecules "acid soluble fraction"	solubility in 5 percent trichloro- acetic acid in the cold	2– 3
Lipids "organic solvent soluble fraction"	solubility in alcohol-ether at 50°C	10–15
Nucleic acids "hot acid soluble fraction"	solubility in 5 percent trichloro- acetic acid at 90°C for 30 minutes	10–20
Proteins "hot acid insoluble fraction"	insolubility in 5 percent trichlo- roacetic acid at 90°C for 30 minutes	55–85

PURIFICATION OF PROTEINS

In order to study a given protein one must prepare it in pure form by separating it from other proteins present in the initial "extract" obtained from living tissue. The procedures used constitute a highly refined and rapidly developing art that we shall not attempt to describe here. The first notable success in the purification of proteins was achieved by James Sumner (1926), who crystallized the protein *urease* from the tissue of the jack bean. This important achievement spelled the end of an era during which biologists had come to regard the protein with an awe that precluded the utilization of straightforward chemical approaches to the study of these complicated compounds. Indeed, many biologists gave Sumner's discovery little credence for a number of years. By now some 75 different proteins have been crystallized and a much larger number have been prepared in highly purified state.

Two special properties of proteins have an important influence on the success of protein purifications. (1) Proteins are labile compounds capable of losing their specific biological properties under a variety of relatively mild chemical and physical treatments (denaturation). Thus after every purification it is necessary to demonstrate that no significant denaturation has occurred. (2) Because of the size of the protein molecule and the loose structure of the protein crystal, a considerable amount of impurity can be included in a crystalline preparation.

In recent years a number of increasingly stringent criteria have been used to evaluate the purity, or "homogeneity," of a protein preparation. Thus, a successful purification of a protein is one that involves a minimum of denaturation and satisfies a variety of criteria of homogeneity.

THE SIZE AND SHAPE OF PROTEIN MOLECULES

The very large size and relative lability of protein molecules present the structural chemist with a number of problems that cannot be solved with the methods applied to small molecules. Consequently, a variety of methods have been developed and refined during the last twenty years that have made it possible to determine with considerable precision the molecular weight and to a lesser extent the shape of macromolecules.

In the ultracentrifuge, for instance, macromolecules can be spun at speeds up to 60,000 rpm., thereby increasing the gravitational force on the molecules to more than 100,000 times gravity. This force, which causes the molecules to "sediment," is counteracted by random diffusion of the molecules. Since the equilibrium between these two forces is related to the molecular weight, the latter can be measured for macromolecules quite accurately. Other methods utilizing the light-scattering properties of macromolecules, the osmotic pressure of protein solutions, the sedimentation rate in a high gravitational field combined with the diffusion coefficient, the x-ray diffraction of protein crystals and direct visualization and counting in the electron microscope, and in some cases direct chemical analysis have also been developed. Table 8-2 lists the molecular weights of a number of proteins and nucleoproteins that have been determined by several methods; it can be seen that, in the main, the values obtained agree very well.

The determination of molecular shape, on the other hand, is still fraught with a number of difficulties. The "hydrodynamic" methods, which are based on the relationship between molecular asymmetry and the frictional force necessary to move the molecules through the solvent, are rapid, precise, and easily carried out. Unfortunately, because of a number of assumptions, these methods yield equivocal results. Electron microscopy and x-ray diffraction methods have, in the last few years, given us spectacular "pictures" of the shape of protein molecules, but the former so far permits clear resolution of the shape of only the larger molecules and the latter has so far been applied to only a very few cases. Fig. 8-1 shows a number of protein molecules as they appear in the electron microscope.

TABLE 8-2

Molecular Weights of a Number of Proteins,
Determined by Several Different Methods

Protein	Osmotic pressure	Light scattering	Sedimentation rate and diffusion	Sedimentation equilibrium	Chemical methods
Insulin	12,000	12,000			6000[a]
Ribonuclease			12,700	13,000	12,000
Pepsin	36,000		35,500	39,000	
Ovalbumin	40,000 46,000	38,000	44,000	40,500 43,500	
Hemoglobin	67,000		63,000		66,800
Bovine serum albumin	69,000	77,000	65,400	68,000	
Hemocyanin (Polynurus)		461,000	450,000	450,000	
Tomato bushy stunt virus	9,000,000		10,600,000	7,600,000	
Tobacco mosaic virus	40,000,000		40,700,000		

[a] The discrepancy in the case of insulin is due to insulin's tendency to dimerize.

Application of the above and other physical methods has resulted in the following picture of gross structure (size and shape) of the protein molecule.

(1) The molecular weight of proteins varies over a wide range (insulin 6000, snail hemocyanin 6,700,000). However, large proteins are generally composed of smaller subunits.

(2) Shapes vary considerably from near spherical to highly asymmetrical (see Fig. 8-1).

(3) Unlike many synthetic polymers, proteins are rigid particles of finite shape.

At the end of this chapter we shall discuss the recent results of the application of x-ray diffraction to the detailed or "fine" structure of two protein molecules, myoglobin and hemoglobin. These studies show that proteins, in

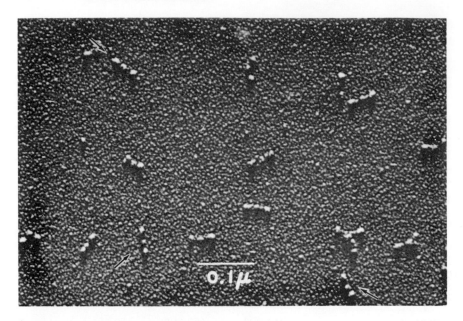

A

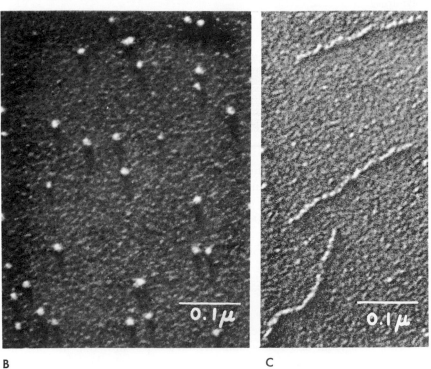

B   C

spite of their tremendous size and complexity, are highly uniform molecules with an extremely precise and definite architecture.

PRIMARY STRUCTURE—THE SEQUENCE OF AMINO ACIDS

When a protein is heated in strong acid at 100°C for several hours, it is broken or hydrolyzed into its constituent building blocks, called amino acids. There are some 20 different amino acids in the proteins of all organisms, although certain proteins may contain fewer of them and certain organisms may contain special amino acids that represent slight modifications of the 20 principle ones. Fig. 8-2 shows the basic structure of all but one of the 20 amino acids. It shows that at neutral pH the amino acid is a "zwitterion," containing simultaneously a negative and positive group. It also shows that the α-carbon atom is asymmetric, since it has four different groups attached to it. All amino acids derived from proteins are l-amino acids (except for glycine, which is not optically active), a fact that strongly suggests the common origin of all living matter on earth. The symbol R in Fig. 8-2 represents the variable portion of the molecule that differentiates one amino acid from the other. Fig. 8-3 is a list of the different R groups of the 20 most common amino acids. Note that the last one, proline, is the only atypical member of the series in the sense that the α-amino group is not free but part of a ring structure. The amino acids are the alphabet of protein structure and are ultimately responsible for the specificity and variability of living matter. The student of biology is well advised to familiarize himself with these important compounds, for the next few decades will witness the elucidation of the precise roles played by the R groups of amino acids in the specific molecular interactions of the cell.

The separation of the 20 amino acids from each other was a formidable task to which the famous chemist Emil Fischer (1852–1919) devoted many years of his life. In 1941 Martin and Synge proposed a new approach to the problem of purification and estimation of compounds that closely resemble each other. This approach involved dissolving the amino acid mixture in a pair of solvents and then "percolating" this mixture along filter paper strips or through columns. By using a second pair of solvents and turning the paper through 90 degrees, it is possible to separate amino acids two dimensionally over a large sheet of filter paper (Fig. 8-4). Because these methods bore some

---

Fig. 8-1 (*facing*).   Shadow-cast electronmicrographs of various protein molecules A: Fibrinogen molecules ($\times$ 150,000). (Courtesy of C. E. Hall and H. S. Slayter, Massachusetts Institute of Technology.) B: Alkaline phosphatase molecules ($\times$ 163,000). (Courtesy of Hall.) C: Collagen molecules ($\times$ 166,000). (Courtesy of Hall and P. Doty.)

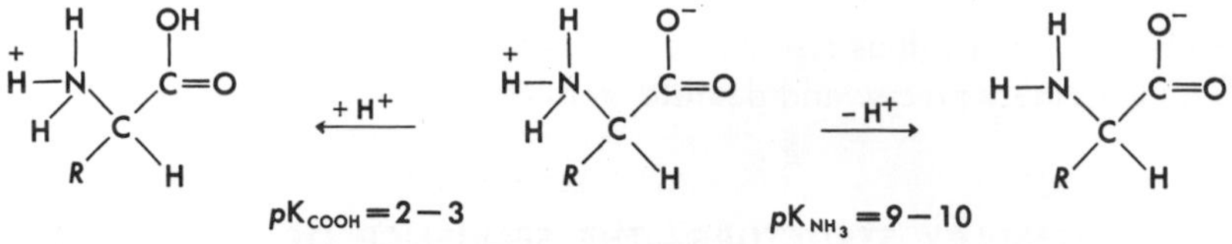

Fig. 8-2. Zwitterion forms of amino acids.

resemblance to a technique employed many years earlier by Tswett to the separation of leaf pigments, Martin and Synge named the procedure *chromatography*. In the last 20 years, chromatographic methods have been extended and perfected to such an extent that they are now the most widely used techniques for analysis and purification. The "ultimate" in amino acid analysis has been achieved in the laboratory of Moore and Stein, who have perfected column chromatography of amino acids and built an automatic machine for their determination. This device is capable of taking the hy-

NONPOLAR (ALIPHATIC)

—H   Glycine (Gly)
—CH_3 Alanine (Ala)

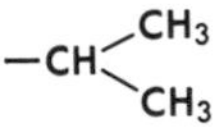

Valine (Val)

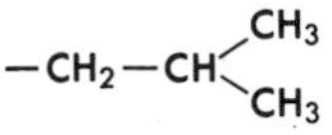

Leucine (Leu)

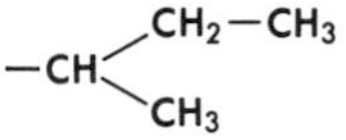

Isoleucine (Ileu)

ALCOHOLIC (ALIPHATIC AND AROMATIC)

—CH_2—OH   Serine (Ser) 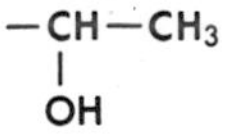
—CH—CH_3 Threonine (Thr)
  |
  OH

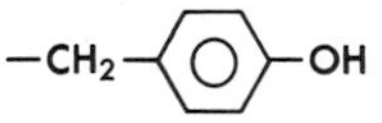

Tyrosine (Tyr)

OTHER AROMATIC

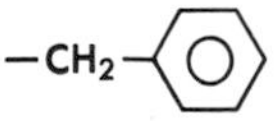

Phenylalanine (Phe)

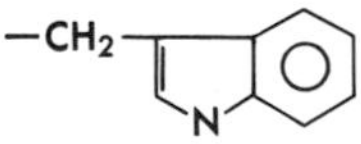

Tryptophan (Try)

AMIDES

—CH_2—$CONH_2$ Asparagine (Asp—NH_2)
—CH_2—CH_2—$CONH_2$ Glutamine (Glu—NH_2)

AMINE BASES

—CH_2—CH_2—CH_2—CH_2—NH_3^+ Lysine (Lys)

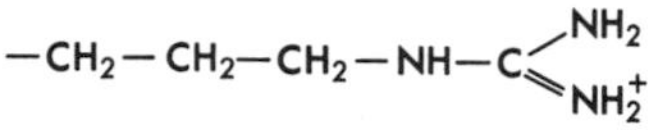

Arginine (Arg)

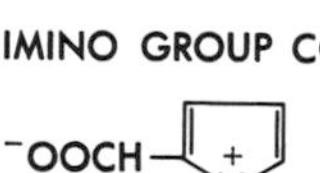

Histidine (His)

SULFUR CONTAINING

—CH_2—SH   Cysteine (CySH)
—CH_2—CH_2—S—CH_3 Methionine (Met)

IMINO GROUP CONTAINING

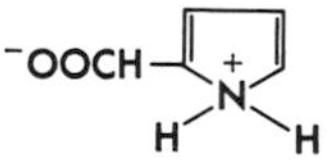

Proline (Pro)

CARBOXYLIC ACIDS

—CH_2—COO^- Aspartic acid (Asp)
—CH_2—CH_2—COO^- Glutamic acid (Glu)

Fig. 8-3. The "R groups" of the 20 commonly occurring amino acids.

drolysate of 1 mg of protein and estimating the concentration of each one of its component amino acids within an accuracy of a few percent. Moore and Stein utilized a column of ion exchange resins made of sulfonated polystyrene. The amino acid preparation is placed on the column in a buffer at low pH and low ionic strength, which are conditions for maximum binding of the positively charged amino acids with the —SO_3^{2-} groups on the resin. Buffer is then run through the column and both the pH and the ionic strength are raised. This process, called elution, causes the different amino acids to percolate down the column at different rates, eventually separating into separate bands. The "eluate" emanating at the bottom of the column is either collected in separate fractions by an automatic *fraction collector* or processed by an automatic machine. In the former case the separate fractions are reacted with a reagent called ninhydrin, which gives a purple color in the presence of amino acids, and the amount of purple color in a colorimeter is estimated; comparison of this result with a standard curve permits calculation of the amino acid concentration. The automatic machine performs the ninhydrin reaction automatically and continuously while a recorder draws on a chart the

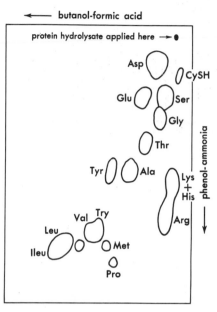

Fig. 8-4. Two-dimensional paper chromatography of amino acids.

color intensity as it passes through the colorimeter. Although at first glance such an automatic procedure might appear to be merely oversophisticated gadgetry, it has in fact been possible to perform during the last few years a number of very important experiments that required both the speed and the precision of these new automatic methods.

Fig. 8-5 represents a chromatogram of an amino acid mixture obtained by the Moore and Stein method. The concentration of each amino acid is proportional to the area under the curve.

Once protein has been hydrolyzed into its building blocks, it is logical to examine how these building blocks fit together in the protein molecule. Fischer was able to show that upon hydrolysis of a protein an equal number of amino and carboxyl groups are released. To explain this result he suggested that the amino acids were linked to each other by a peptide bond (Fig. 8-6). The equilibrium of this reaction is far on the hydrolysis side, and

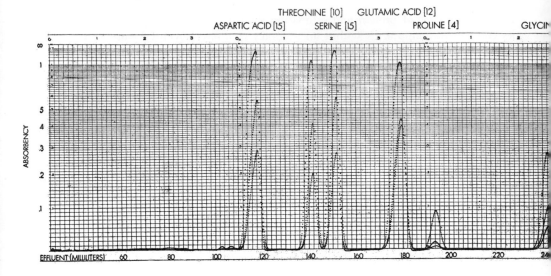

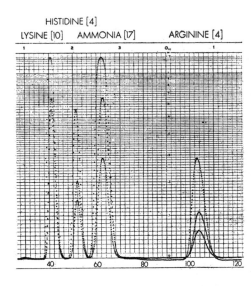

Fig. 8-5. Column chromatography of amino acids using the Moore and Stein automatic amino acid analyzer. Note that analysis is performed at 3 levels of sensitivity. The analysis is of a hydrolyzed sample of the protein ribonuclease. (Reprinted with permission. Copyright © 1961 by Scientific American, Inc. All rights reserved.)

as we shall see later, the cell synthesizes the peptide bond during protein synthesis by an entirely different mechanism. Fischer's peptide bond theory for protein structure has since been validated by many separate lines of evidence. Proteolytic enzymes, for instance, which are known to break the peptide bond of synthetic peptides, are also capable of hydrolyzing proteins.

Fig. 8-7 is a diagram of a hypothetical chain of amino acids termed a polypeptide. Notice that except for the terminal carboxyl (C-terminal) and the terminal amino (N-terminal) groups, all the remaining α-carboxyl and

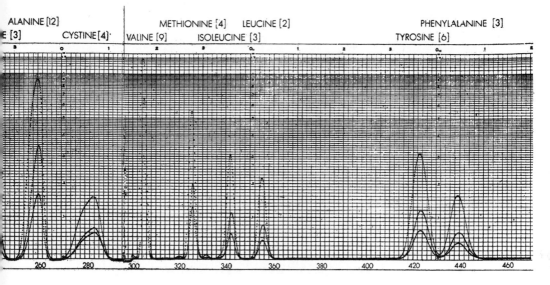

ALANINE [12]   METHIONINE [4]   LEUCINE [2]   PHENYLALANINE [3]
E [3]   CYSTINE [4]   VALINE [9]   ISOLEUCINE [3]   TYROSINE [6]

260   280   300   320   340   360   380   400   420   440   460

α-amino groups are involved in the amide linkage. This linkage is not capable of releasing or accepting protons and therefore does not contribute to the acid-base properties of the polypeptide. The electrochemical properties at physiological pH of the polypeptide (and hence of the protein) are determined by the R groups of the acidic amino acids, aspartic acid and glutamic acid, the basic amino acids, lysine and arginine, and by histidine. The latter is important because it is the only amino acid, with the exception of the N-terminal amino group, with a pK in the region of physiological pH, and thus it is the only amino acid that could contribute to a change in charge on the protein caused by small changes in pH under physiological conditions. The role of this amino acid in a mechanism for cellular regulation has yet to be discovered.

The hypothetical polypeptide in Fig. 8-7 shows all the R groups that contribute to the charge on a protein at physiological pH. It shows by extrapolation that a protein is a polyvalent ion containing a number of positive and

glycine   alanine   glycyl-alanine

amide linkage   peptide bond

$-H_2O$
$+H_2O$

Fig. 8-6. The peptide bond.

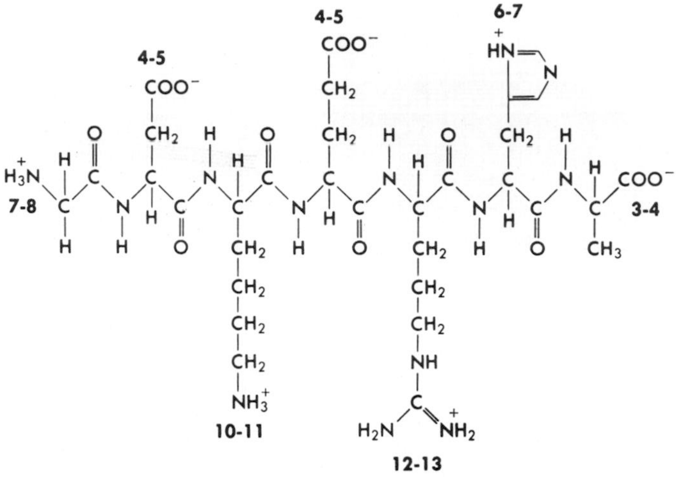

glycyl-aspartyl-lysyl-glutamyl-arginyl-histidyl-alanine

Fig. 8-7. A hypothetical polypeptide containing all the groups that normally contribute charges to proteins. The numbers represent the pK range of each dissociating group.

negative charges. From the dissociation properties of the groups one can predict what should happen when acid or base is added to a protein. Thus when acid is added, —COO⁻ will change to —COOH and therefore leave the protein with a net positive charge; when base is added, —NH₃⁺ will change to —NH₂, leaving the protein with a net negative charge. At a certain intermediate pH called the *isoelectric point* the number of positive charges equals the number of negative charges. Since most proteins have isoelectric points on the acid side, they will carry a net negative charge at physiological pH. However, the protamines and histones, which are proteins found on the chromosomes, contain large amounts of lysine and arginine and they therefore carry a net positive charge under normal conditions. Without a doubt this property plays an important role in the molecular structure of the chromosome, which in part is composed of positively charged proteins interacting with negatively charged DNA.

We have shown that it is possible to determine the amino acid composition of a polypeptide. Is it possible, however, to determine the specific sequence of amino acids in the polypeptide? Sanger was the first to show that this indeed could be done. As is usually the case with a *first* contribution in a given field, his achievement is notable not only for the very important technical contribution made in answering this question, nor just for the far-reaching theoretical conclusions deriving from the results, but also in the insight and faith involved in asking the particular question. The early traditions of protein chemistry derive from colloid chemistry, which regarded its materials as chemically indefinite entities to be characterized by statistical rather than precise chemical parameters. Sanger challenged this tradition by asking a question that as recently as 1945 was considered preposterous by most protein chemists. He asked: "Do proteins have a specific and finite chemical composition down to the *sequence* of the 20 building blocks?" To ask such a question and to be willing to invest ten years of one's life in answering it implies a belief in the *absolute* accuracy by which biological macromolecules are replicated and synthesized. The extent to which we take this for granted today is a tribute to the magnitude of Sanger's contribution. When Sanger began his epoch-making study on the protein *insulin*, the method of paper chromatography for the separation of amino acids had just been developed by Martin and Synge. To this Sanger added a technique of his own, the "labeling" of the amino end group (N-terminal group) of a peptide by combining it with the yellow compound 2,4-dinitrofluorobenzene (DNFB) to give a dinitrophenyl (DNP) peptide.

2,4-dinitrofluoro-
benzene
(DNFB)

N-terminal end
of peptide

dinitrophenyl
peptide
(DNP)

This yellow compound is stable during the hydrolysis of the peptide and it is possible by the use of chromatographic separation after hydrolysis to identify the particular amino acid to which the DNP is attached. By determining the N-terminal amino acid it was possible for Sanger to orient the peptide, that is, to distinguish one end from the other. Sanger also developed a number of methods for partially hydrolyzing the insulin molecule into peptides of various lengths. He developed chromatographic procedures for separating these peptides from each other, which permitted him to determine their amino acid composition and the identity of the N-terminal amino acid. Some of the longer peptides had to be hydrolyzed for a second time, chromatographed, and again analyzed for end groups.. As the data accumulated, more and more of the sequence became uniquely defined. Eventually *all* of the sequence had become uniquely defined, after which time all the new data simply verified the existing structure without providing any evidence against it. Fig. 8-8 is a summary of the results that Sanger used in determining the amino acid sequence of one of the polypeptide chains of the insulin molecule.

	N-terminal end																
PEPTIDES FROM ACID HYDROLYZATES	Phe · Val		Glu · His			CySO₃H · Gly			His · Leu			Glu · Ala					

PEPTIDES FROM ACID HYDROLYZATES

Phe · Val Glu · His CySO₃H · Gly His · Leu Glu · Ala
Val · Asp His · Leu Leu · Val Ala
Asp · Glu Leu · CySO₃H Ser · His Val · Glu
Phe · Val · Asp Leu · CySO₃H · Gly Val · Glu · Ala
Glu · His · Leu Ser · His · Leu
Val · Asp · Glu Leu · Val · Glu
His · Leu · CySO₃H Ala
Phe · Val · Asp · Glu Ser · His · Leu · Val
His · Leu · CySO₃H · Gly Leu · Val · Glu · Ala
Phe · Val · Asp · Glu · His Ser · His · Leu · Val · Glu
Glu · His · Leu · CySO₃H His · Leu · Vol · Glu
Ser · His · Leu · Val · Glu · Ala

SEQUENCES DEDUCED FROM THE ABOVE PEPTIDES

Phe · Val · Asp · Glu · His · Leu · CySO₃H · Gly
Ser · His · Leu · Val · Glu · Ala

PEPTIDES FROM PEPSIN HYDROLYZATE

Phe · Val · Asp · Glu · His · Leu · CySO₃H · Gly · Ser · His · Leu
     | |
    NH₂ NH₂
Val · Glu · Ala
His · Leu · CySO₃H · Gly · Ser · His · Leu

PEPTIDES FROM CHYMOTRYPSIN HYDROLYZATE

Phe · Val · Asp · Glu · His · Leu · CySO₃H · Gly · Ser · His · Leu · Val · Glu · Ala
     | |
    NH₂ NH₂

PEPTIDES FROM TRYPSIN HYDROLYZATE

STRUCTURE OF PHENYLALANYL CHAIN OF OXIDIZED INSULIN

Phe · Val · Asp · Glu · His · Leu · CySO₃H · Gly · Ser · His · Leu · Val · Glu · Ala
     | |
    NH₂ NH₂

N-terminal end

Fig. 8-8. Compilation of Sanger's analytical results showing how the final sequence of one of the polypeptide chains of insulin was deduced.

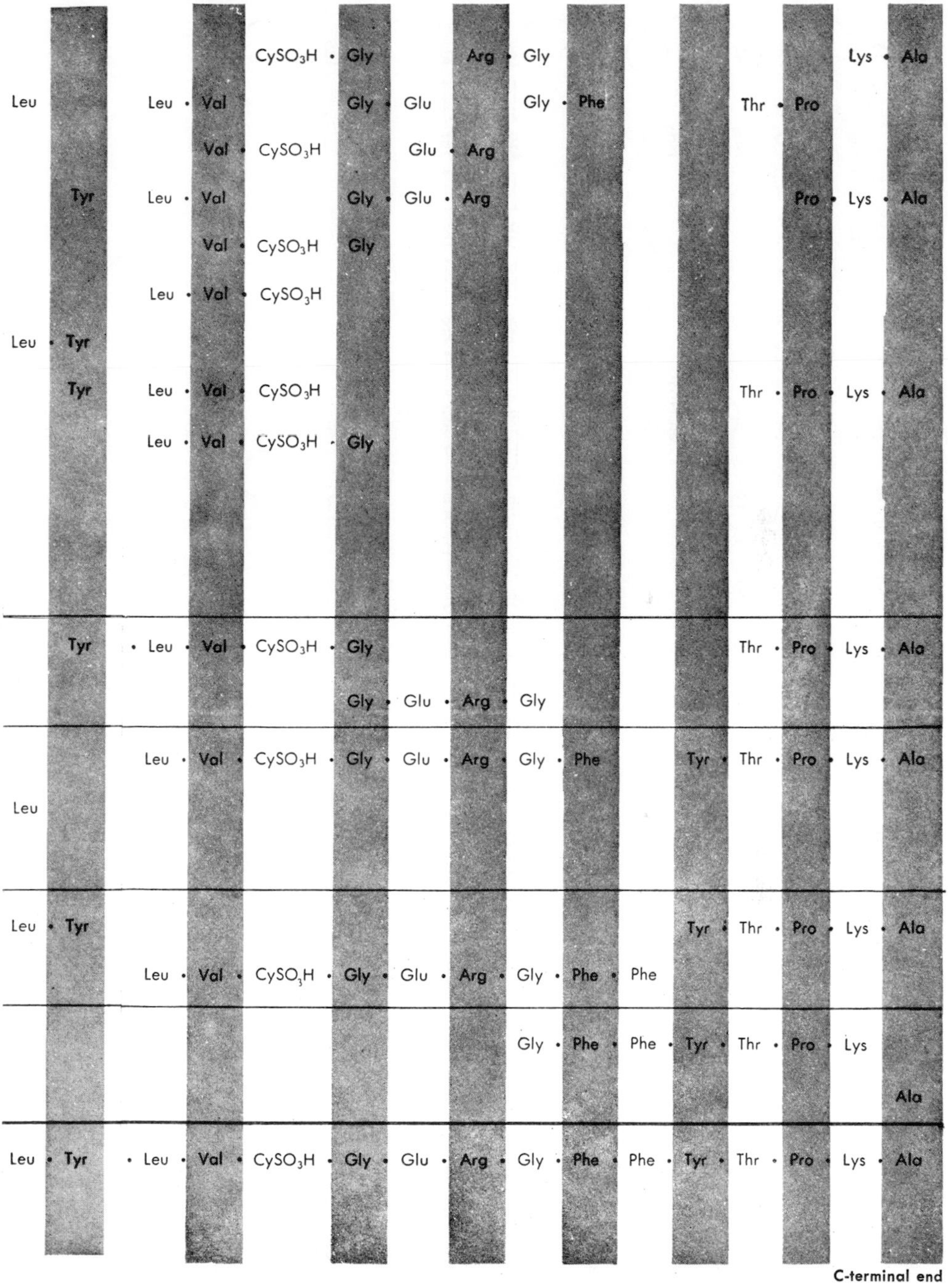

Leu

Leu · Val   CySO$_3$H · Gly   Arg · Gly   Lys · Ala

Gly · Glu   Gly · Phe   Thr · Pro

Val · CySO$_3$H   Glu · Arg

Tyr   Leu · Val   Gly · Glu · Arg   Pro · Lys · Ala

Val · CySO$_3$H   Gly

Leu · Val · CySO$_3$H

Leu · Tyr

Tyr   Leu · Val · CySO$_3$H   Thr · Pro · Lys · Ala

Leu · Val · CySO$_3$H · Gly

Tyr   · Leu · Val · CySO$_3$H · Gly   Thr · Pro · Lys · Ala

Gly · Glu · Arg · Gly

Leu · Val · CySO$_3$H · Gly · Glu · Arg · Gly · Phe   Tyr · Thr · Pro · Lys · Ala

Leu

Leu · Tyr   Tyr · Thr · Pro · Lys · Ala

Leu · Val · CySO$_3$H · Gly · Glu · Arg · Gly · Phe · Phe

Gly · Phe · Phe · Tyr · Thr · Pro · Lys

Ala

Leu · Tyr   · Leu · Val · CySO$_3$H · Gly · Glu · Arg · Gly · Phe · Phe · Tyr · Thr · Pro · Lys · Ala

C-terminal end

(Reprinted with permission.   Copyright © 1955 by Scientific American, Inc. All rights reserved.)

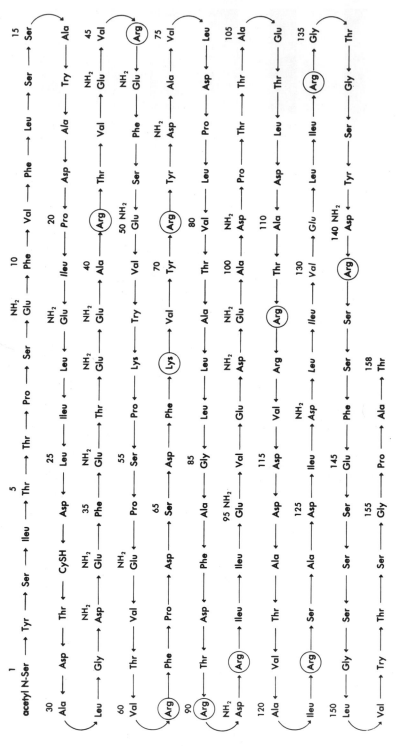

Fig. 8-9. Primary structure of the protein of the tobacco mosaic virus. Circles are placed around the lysine and arginine residues that are on the N-terminal side of the peptide bond cleaved by trypsin. (Courtesy of Virus Laboratory, University of California.)

Using the above approach, Sanger was able to show that only one finite sequence would satisfy the data he had obtained. It was shown the first time that, despite the complexity of the protein molecule, the cell is able to synthesize it in a reproducible and chemically precise manner. It is interesting to note that although insulin is one of the smallest proteins we know, it is not the simplest in structure since it is composed of two polypeptides. Fig. 8-9 shows the sequence or so-called primary structure of a much larger protein (18,000 molecular weight) that is composed of a single chain. The determination of sequence of this larger polypeptide proved a much more difficult problem requiring the precision of the automated column chromatographic method of Moore and Stein.

The primary structure of a number of other proteins has now been determined, and although the largest polypeptide chain, possibly of molecular weight of 60,000, has yet to be tackled, it is fair to say that we are well on our way to a general solution of this problem.

SECONDARY STRUCTURE—
THE RELATIONSHIP OF NEAREST NEIGHBORS

Physical studies of protein molecules have shown that they are compact, rigid, not overly elongated molecules. The conclusion must be that the polypeptide is folded in some manner to achieve this compact structure, but the precise geometry of folding has been a subject of many years of speculation. In 1951 Pauling and Corey provided the first clue. They had started their work with a meticulous x-ray analysis of the structure of a number of simple peptides, which yielded a precise description of the amide linkage of the polypeptide chain (Fig. 8-10). They discovered that the six atoms of the amide group (CCONHC) are "coplanar," lying within a few

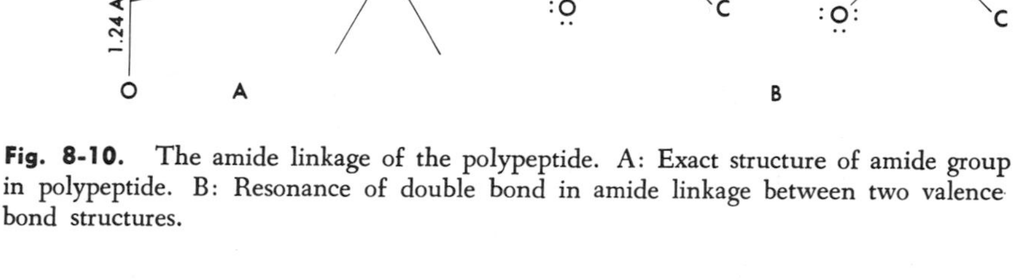

Fig. 8-10.   The amide linkage of the polypeptide. A: Exact structure of amide group in polypeptide. B: Resonance of double bond in amide linkage between two valence bond structures.

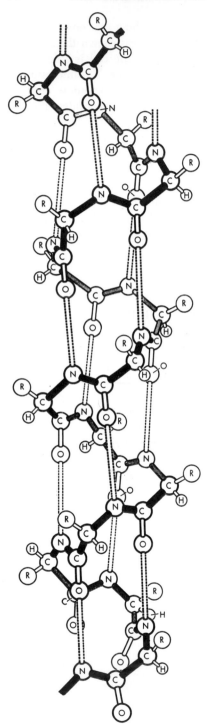

one hundredths of an Ångstrom unit in a common plane. The planarity of the amide group, as well as the short distance of the peptide (C—N) linkage, Pauling explained by a resonance of the C=O double bond as shown in Fig. 8-10, the actual structure being a hybrid of the two states. Furthermore, they found that the amide group was arranged in the *trans*-configuration; that is, the two asymmetric carbon atoms lie in the opposite corners of the group. Finally, Pauling and his associates pointed out that the bonds to the corner carbons of the amide group are single chemical bonds and therefore capable of rotation. They argued that it is rotation around this bond that would determine the configuration of the polypeptide. By building scale models they soon discovered that a large number of different configurations could be generated if one accepted the above restrictions. It is precisely here, in deciding which of these many configurations is the most likely to occur, that Pauling made the crucial intuitive leap. Having had a great deal of experience with the importance of hydrogen bonds in the crystal structure of model compounds, Pauling predicted that the preferred configuration of the polypeptide would be the one that favored maximum hydrogen bonding between the —C=O

Fig. 8-11. Model of an α helix, a configuration of the polypeptide chain believed to occur in proteins. The backbone of the chain consists of repeating sequences of C, C, N. R represents side chains of the different amino acids. The broken lines represent hydrogen bonds that stabilize the helix. (Reprinted with permission. Copyright © 1961 by Scientific American, Inc. All rights reserved.)

and —NH groups of the amide linkage. He very wisely, as a first approximation, decided to ignore the possible effects of the R groups. He then discovered that by subjecting each amide group along the polypeptide to a small rotation, a helix was generated that had the property of forming hydrogen bonds across the turns of the helix. The so-called α *helix* (Fig. 8-11) is capable of forming hydrogen bonds between all its amide groups, a fact that on a priori grounds would give it the greatest degree of stability. The characteristics of the α helix can be described by stating the number of amino acid residues per turn (3.6), the pitch of the helix (5.4 A), the diameter including the side chains (10.5 A), and the number of amino acid residues in one hydrogen-bonded loop (3). These dimensions and several others were looked for in a number of proteins and synthetic polypeptides by the method of x-ray analysis, and a great deal of evidence soon accumulated to bear out Pauling's brilliant analysis. As we shall see later, there is now even more direct evidence for the existence of the α helix in proteins.

TERTIARY STRUCTURE— THE CONFORMATION OF THE POLYPEPTIDE

As we have already said, proteins are compact, rigid molecules (Fig. 8-1). Although the formation of an α helix would shorten the extended polypeptide chain, this would by no means give a compact, near-spherical molecule. Thus the dimensions of an α helix of the protein of tobacco mosaic virus would be 6 × 240 A when in actual fact it is approximately 75 × 25 A. We therefore must imagine that the α helix bends and folds in such a way as to make a more compact structure. Furthermore, we must also take into account that amino end group labeling with DNP of entire proteins showed that some proteins contain more than one polypeptide chain. We think of *tertiary structure* as the folding and turning of the polypeptide chain, mostly in the α-helix configuration, to form a compact structure. The association of two or more compact polypeptide units to form the fully fashioned protein molecule (in the case where more than one polypeptide occurs in a molecule) has recently been termed *quaternary structure*.

The questions raised by tertiary and quaternary protein structure are not yet completely answered. What properties of the polypeptide chain could account for tertiary and quaternary structure? So far we have ignored the R groups and have said that they are not important in α-helix formation. It now appears, however, that they are extremely important in the "conformation" or winding around of the α helix. Certain R groups are capable of interacting with each other, and when this happens they can be expected to help stabilize an α-helix loop by forming points of attachment in certain places. The list of specific interactions between R groups is as yet unreliable and incomplete, and will ultimately require many additions and revisions. The following is a list of certain types of interactions that are believed to occur and for which there is evidence in some cases.

(1) *Disulfide bonds.* The disulfide is the only other covalent bond frequently found in proteins. It is formed when two —SH groups of cysteine react with each other in the following manner.

$$2SH + \tfrac{1}{2}O_2 = \text{—S—S—} + H_2O$$

It is interesting to note that Sanger discovered three such bonds in the insulin molecule, one connecting two portions of the same peptide and the other two holding the two peptides of the insulin molecule together (Fig. 8-12). In the ribonuclease molecule, on the other hand, there is only one polypeptide chain and four disulfide groups formed within that chain (Fig. 8-13).

(2) *Hydrogen bonds.* The extent to which hydrogen bonds between R groups are responsible for tertiary and quaternary structure is at present a vigorously debated issue. Substantial evidence points to the formation of hydrogen bonds between tyrosyl and histidyl, and between seryl and aspartyl residues.

(3) *Hydrophobic bonds.* A substantial proportion (35 to 45 percent) of the R groups of proteins are of the nonpolar, hydrophobic variety (valine, leucine, isoleucine, phenylalanine, proline, tryptophan, alanine). Kauzmann has suggested that these nonpolar side chains are likely to remove themselves from the aqueous medium and seek each other to form one or more "hydrophobic regions" in the molecule. The force stabilizing this interaction is not only the so-called Van der Waal attraction between the nonpolar side chains but is also due to the increased ability for water around the protein molecule to form hydrogen bonds owing to the withdrawal of the nonpolar groups from the aqueous phase.

(4) *Salt linkages.* Since at physiological pH, the R groups of lysine and arginine are positively charged and those of aspartic and glutamic acid are negatively charged, it has been suggested that salt linkages might form be-

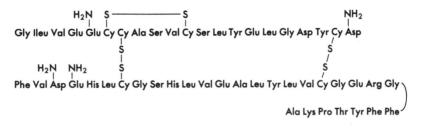

Fig. 8-12. The structure of insulin, showing *intrachain* and *interchain* disulfide bonds. (Sanger.)

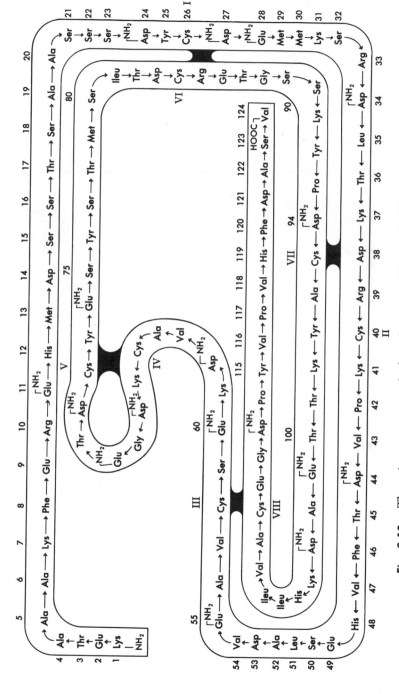

Fig. 8-13. The primary structure of ribonuclease, showing the disulfide bonds cross linking different parts of the single peptide chain (from Smythe, Moore, and Stein). (*J. Biol. Chem*, 1963.)

tween them to stabilize the tertiary and quaternary structures. The titration of proteins and other lines of evidence suggest that if any, only a small proportion of the charged groups contribute to stable bonds not screened out by the salt found in solutions of proteins. It has been suggested that a few salt linkages may be of importance and may be stabilized by nearby hydrophobic regions that protect them from screening effects of the ions in solution.

The research of Kendrew, Perutz, and their associates on the x-ray crystallography of myoglobin and hemoglobin constitutes the most recent and most spectacular development concerning the structural chemistry of the protein molecule. From their work, detailed and precise knowledge of the three-dimensional structure of these molecules is gradually emerging. It is

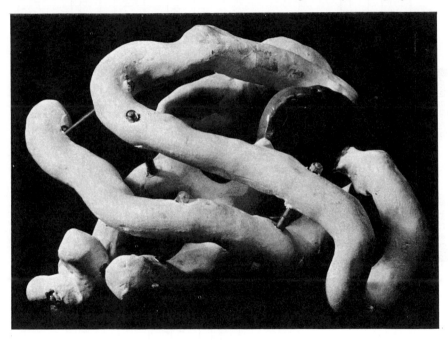

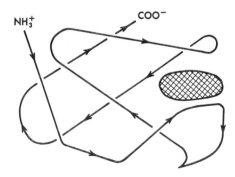

Fig. 8-14. Model of myoglobin at 6 A resolution. The heme group is the shaded flat section at upper right. (Photo by George Rodger. © 1963 Magnum Photos.)

not possible here to discuss in any detail the method of x-ray crystallography employed for the solution of this problem, and the student is advised to read carefully Kendrew's article on the subject (see Suggested Reading List). It suffices to say that these workers were successful in applying the so-called "isomorphous replacement method," which involves comparing crystals of the

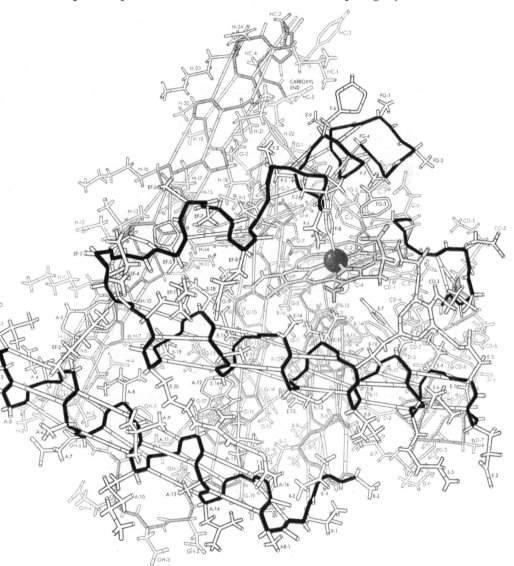

Fig. 8-15. Three-dimensional model of myoglobin based on x-ray analysis at 1.5 A resolution. A number of α-helical structures can be recognized (black). (Reprinted with permission. Copyright © 1961 by Scientific American, Inc. All rights reserved.)

proteins with similar crystals that have had electron-scattering heavy metals introduced in specific regions on the protein molecule. This comparison permits the crystallographer to eliminate specific uncertainties and to deduce the structure directly without guesswork or trial and error.

Kendrew has been able to build a complete model of the myoglobin molecule at a resolution of 6 A. At this level of resolution one sees a complex intestine-shaped mass composed of eight lengths of straight "sausages" interrupted by bends of varying degrees of abruptness (Fig. 8-14). Myoglobin is a colored protein containing a so-called heme group, similar to the one found in hemoglobin, which is responsible for the color and is the site of the oxygen-combining property of the protein. The location of the flat heme group can be clearly seen in the model. The "sausages" turn out to be hollow and to have the same diameters as the Pauling α helix.

Work at a resolution of 1.5 A is now progressing (Fig. 8-15). This involves making about 600 times as many measurements as at 6 A resolution. Computations are so complex and numerous (100,000 electron densities have to be calculated) that the fastest electronic computers are required. Nevertheless, a great deal has already been learned at the 1.5 A level of resolution. The straight lengths of sausage can definitely be recognized as α helixes, a confirmation of Pauling's prediction. It has also been possible to recognize a goodly proportion of the amino acid residues and hence obtain the primary structure. A number of interactions between R groups emerge. Thus Kendrew was able to determine the proximity of a number of groups that had previously been suspected of being involved in such interactions. These include groups capable of forming hydrogen bonds, salt linkages, and hydrophobic bonds. Assuming that is is possible to extrapolate from protein molecules in crystals to protein molecules in solution, it is likely that such data will prove increasingly important in understanding how tertiary and quaternary structure is stabilized.

We are only at the very beginning of this phenomenal breakthrough in our understanding of protein structure and we can expect a great deal from this development. The molecular biology of the cell will one day be understood in terms of the precise interactions between the various molecules composing it. The proteins, being the structural material as well as the catalytic regulators of the cell, play a crucial role in all cell interactions, be they protein-protein, protein-nucleic acid, protein-lipid, or enzyme-substrate interaction. In order to understand these in detail we shall require a highly exact picture of the protein molecule. The progress in this area is a scientific revolution of first magnitude that we are privileged to observe at close range.

SUGGESTED READING LIST

EDSALL, J. T., and WYMAN, J., *Biophysical chemistry*. New York: Academic Press.

HAUROWITZ, F., 1950. *Chemistry and biology of proteins*. New York: Academic Press.

KENDREW, J. C., "Three-dimensional study of a protein," *Scientific American*, December 1961.

NEURATH, H., and BAILEY, K., 1953–1954. *The proteins*. New York: Academic Press.

PAULING, L., COREY, R. B., and HAYWORD, R., "The structure of protein molecules," *Scientific American*, July 1954.

STEIN, W. H., and MOORE, S., "The chemical structure of proteins," *Scientific American*, March 1961.

THOMPSON, E. O. P., "The insulin molecule," *Scientific American*, May 1955.

PART III

BIOLOGICAL
DYNAMICS

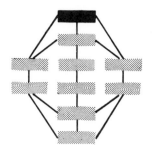

CHAPTER NINE

ENZYME CATALYSIS, A MECHANISM OF BIOLOGICAL CONTROL

We pointed out in Chapter 6 that most organic compounds of the cell are remarkably stable at physiological temperatures, pressures, and hydrogen ion concentrations. If urea, for instance, is dissolved in water, it will not react with its solvent at an appreciable rate even though to do so would release a considerable amount of energy.

$$\begin{matrix} H_2N \\ \\ H_2N \end{matrix}\!\!\!\!\!>\!\!C=O + H_2O \longrightarrow CO_2 + 2NH_3 + 13,800\ \text{calories}$$

Eyring's explanation is that the urea and water do not react at an appreciable rate because the reaction has to pass through an "activated complex," the formation of which takes a great deal of energy (Fig. 9-1). Thus in order to form the activated complex, water and urea molecules must collide with a certain minimum amount of energy. As Fig. 9-2 shows, only an infinitesimal number of urea and water molecules have this minimum amount of energy at room temperature. By raising the temperature, a larger proportion of molecules will achieve this minimal energy and the rate of the reaction will increase correspondingly. This is what the laboratory organic chemist does, though he also at times varies the pressure and utilizes extremes of acidity or alkalinity in order to speed up the rate of organic reactions. But the cell carries out its reactions at mild temperatures, low pressures, and low

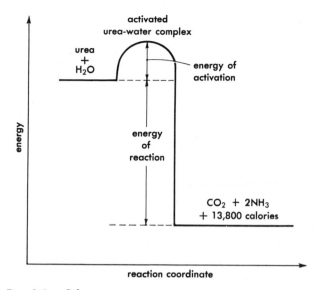

Fig. 9-1. Schematic representation of the energetics of urea hydrolysis. In order to react with water a urea molecule must have sufficient energy to form an activated urea-water complex.

acidity and alkalinity, often at considerable rates. Furthermore the cell is able to *control* these reactions and to synchronize them with respect to each other. These mysterious powers of the cell are due to the *specific biological catalysis* carried out by enzymes.

Catalysis was defined by the chemists van't Hoff and Ostwald as the speeding up of a reaction without affecting the results of the over-all reaction. Subsequent work has made it clear that the catalyst does react with the "*substrate*" and is regenerated at the end in its original form. This enables the catalyst to go through many cycles of reaction, and explains why it is effective in such very low concentrations. The substrate-catalyst complex has

Fig. 9-2. Energy distribution of urea in water at two temperatures, in relation to activation energy necessary for hydrolysis of urea. At 100°C a much higher proportion of molecules have energies equal to or greater than the activation energy.

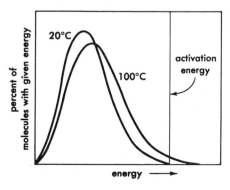

an energy of formation lower than that of the "activated" intermediates of the uncatalyzed reaction, thus permitting a larger number of molecules to react at a given temperature (Fig. 9-3). It should be noted that since the formation of the catalyst-substrate intermediate is temporary, having nothing to do with the initial and final states, it has absolutely no effect on the equilibrium of the reaction. Catalysts are not thermodynamic genii capable of pushing reactions "uphill." They *do not shift equilibria,* but merely increase the rate at which the equilibrium is reached.

Biological catalysis by enzymes obeys the same general rules observed for nonenzymatic catalysis. It differs from other forms of catalysis chiefly in the greater effectiveness of lowering the energy barrier of activation (see Fig. 9-3) and in the extraordinary degree of specificity exhibited. Herein lies a clue to the delicate control of cell processes that enzymes exert. This control is possible because enzymes can act at very low concentration and with a high degree of specificity. By regulating the supply of tiny amounts of active enzyme the cell can control the metabolic flux of the compounds within it. Thus the function of biological catalysis is not only the speeding up of chemical reactions but perhaps more importantly their regulation. In order to understand their regulatory capacity we must first study the general properties of enzymes.

THE ENZYME ASSAY

Modern biochemistry owes its success to the specificity of enzyme action. This in practice permits us to mix a purified substrate with enzyme

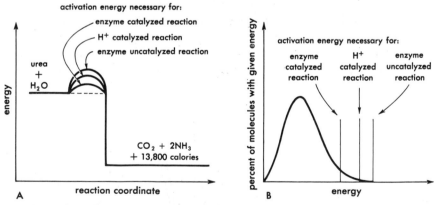

Fig. 9-3. A: Schematic representation showing that an enzyme-catalyzed reaction has lower energy of formation of activated complex than does an H^+ catalyzed or uncatalyzed reaction. B: Schematic representation showing the effect of the lower energy of activation on the number of molecules with sufficient energy to form activated complex.

preparations that might contain 1000 times as much impurity, and obtain a quantitative assay of the amount of enzyme present. The reason for this, as we have indicated, is that the enzyme can ignore all the extraneous compounds and catalyze specifically the reactions of its substrate. It is possible, for instance, to grind up some jack beans and add this crude preparation to purified urea. The hydrolysis of the urea can then be followed by measuring the production of ammonia with an appropriate chemical test (Fig. 9-4). The practice usually followed is to draw a tangent to the curve with its origin at zero time. The slope of this line is called the initial rate of the reaction and is related to the enzyme concentration. To estimate the purity of an enzyme preparation, the initial rate is divided by the total amount of protein present. This measure is called the *specific activity* and it increases as successive steps of purification provide a purer enzyme preparation. When the specific activity cannot be increased beyond a certain limit, even though a wide range of purification procedures have been employed, it is generally assumed that the enzyme is pure. This may or may not be the case, depending on the stringency of the criteria used for judging purity.

THE PROTEIN NATURE OF ENZYMES

The general procedure we have just outlined was employed by Sumner, who in 1926 was the first to crystallize an enzyme, urease. This achievement was especially remarkable because it took place at a time when an atmosphere of awe surrounded the phenomenon of biological catalysis.

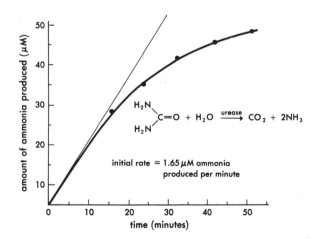

Fig. 9-4. The rate of production of ammonia by the action of urease on urea and water. The slope of the straight line represents the initial rate.

The crystals of urease that Sumner obtained proved to be made of protein, but owing to the prestige of the great chemist Willstätter, who opposed the notion that enzymes were "mere" proteins, it took a great deal of further experimentation before the protein nature of enzymes became generally accepted. By 1956 some 75 enzymes had been crystallized and a great many more had been purified, and all of them were found to contain protein. Perhaps the most convincing proof for the protein nature of enzymes is the often repeated experiment whereby a given enzyme is treated with a protein-digesting enzyme (proteinase). It can be shown that the loss of enzyme activity parallels the disappearance of protein. It is possible also to demonstrate a parallelism between protein denaturation, as caused by a number of agents, and loss of enzyme activity.

In the last few years, occasional claims have been made for enzymatic activity of preparations containing no protein. None of these claims has ever been fully repeated or substantiated, however, and it must therefore be concluded that the protein nature of enzymes is fully established.

The fact that enzymes are proteins has a number of consequences related to their properties. One of these is the effect of temperature on enzyme action. Fig. 9-5 shows that this effect has two components: a curve with a positive slope, which is caused by the effect of temperature on a chemical

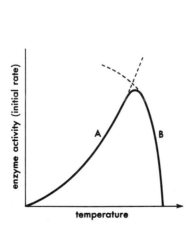
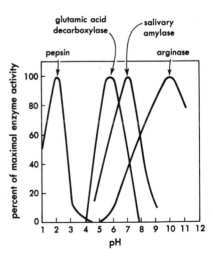

Fig. 9-5 (*left*). The effect of temperature on enzyme activity. The curve is a composite of two processes. *A* is the effect of temperature on the enzyme-catalyzed reaction. *B* is the effect of temperature on the rate of denaturation of the enzyme. **Fig. 9-6** (*right*). Effect of pH on the activity of a number of enzymes. (Redrawn from J. S. Fruton and S. Simmonds, *General Biochemistry*, Wiley, 1953. With permission.)

reaction (see Fig. 9-2), and a curve with a very steep downward slope, which is due to the effect of temperature on the denaturation of the enzyme. The marked effect of temperature on denaturation is a unique and characteristic property of proteins and nucleic acids.

Since proteins are polyvalent, positively and negatively charged ions, they are very sensitive to changes in pH that not only change the dissociation of certain *R* groups presumably involved in the catalytic process but have also been shown to cause more far-reaching structural changes in the protein molecule. Because of this dual effect, enzymes exhibit very sharp pH optima which occur over a relatively wide range of pH values (Fig. 9-6).

For a number of reasons, enzymes are not always found in an active state. Some enzymes, among them the proteolytic, or protein-digesting variety, are often found in the cell as inactive precursors. *Trypsingen*, for instance, is inactive but can be activated to *trypsin* by a number of enzymes, including trypsin itself. The activation seems to involve the removal of a short peptide, followed by some structural changes in the protein molecule that finally yield the active trypsin enzyme. Other enzymes, as we have already pointed out in Chapter 4, require for activity certain divalent cations like Ca^{2+}, Zn^{2+}, Mn^{2+}, Mg^{2+}, or Co^{2+}. Another category of enzymes requires as a "coenzyme" a complicated, organic compound. Both the divalent cation and the coenzyme can usually be separated from the enzyme by *dialysis*. This procedure involves putting the protein into a cellophane bag with pores too small to allow the enzyme to go through, and surrounding it with large volumes of water or salt solution. The coenzyme is able to pass through the pores of the dialysis bag and become diluted in the large external volume of solution. The coenzyme is usually stable in boiling water while the *apoenzyme*, or protein portion of the active enzyme, is inactivated by heat. Dialyzability and heat stability are, then, the usual tests for a coenzyme. Some enzymes, however, contain a nonprotein portion that is sufficiently firmly attached so that it cannot be removed by dialysis. This nonprotein portion, called the *prosthetic group*, plays an important role in the interaction between enzyme and substrate.

THE ENZYME-SUBSTRATE COMPLEX

If the activity of an enzyme is measured at a number of different substrate concentrations (Fig. 9-7A) and if the rate of reaction is plotted against substrate concentration, a curve depicted in Fig. 9-7B is obtained. As the substrate concentration is increased, the value of v approaches a limiting velocity, V. At this velocity enzyme activity is proportional to enzyme concentration. To explain these relationships, Henri (1920) first suggested that

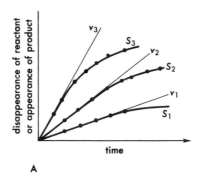
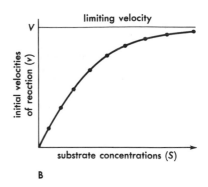

Fig. 9-7.   A: Initial rates of reactions (v_1, v_2, v_3) at three substrate concentrations (S_1, S_2, S_3). B: Curve obtained when initial velocities of enzyme-catalyzed reactions at different substrate concentrations are plotted against substrate concentrations. Limiting velocity (V) is the initial velocity at "infinite" substrate concentration.

the enzyme and substrate combine with each other. Thus it can be seen on qualitative grounds that only when the substrate concentration is high enough to keep the enzyme fully occupied with the catalytic process does the proportionality between enzyme activity and enzyme concentration occur. Michaelis and Menten (1913) were able to validate Henri's hunch in quantitative terms. They began their formulation by assuming that the *law of mass action* applied to the formation of an enzyme-substrate complex, and obtained the following relationship.

$$v = \frac{V\,[S]}{K_m + [S]}$$

where v = velocity of the enzymatic reaction

V = the limiting or maximal velocity at "infinite" substrate concentration

$[S]$ = the substrate concentration in moles per liter of solution

K_m = the Michaelis constant in moles per liter of solution

If the Michaelis-Menten equation is plotted (Fig. 9-8), a rectangular hyperbola is obtained with a shape quite similar to the experimental curve shown in Fig. 9-7B. This, in itself, is a neat experimental validation of the enzyme-substrate complex assumed in the derivation. There is now a great deal more direct spectroscopic evidence for the existence of the enzyme-substrate complex.

The curve in Fig. 9-8 shows, as can be checked by simple algebraic substitution, that at a velocity of half the limiting value, $[S]$ is equal to K_m.

Although K_m is not a strict measure of affinity between enzyme and substrate, it is nevertheless a rough approximation of it. From Fig. 9-8 it can be seen that the lower the value of K_m—that is, the steeper the slope of the curve—the greater the approximate affinity between enzyme and substrate.

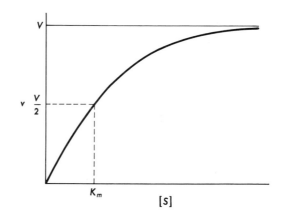

Fig. 9-8. Curve obtained by plotting the Michaelis-Menten equation. Note that the shape of this curve is very similar to the experimental curve shown in Fig. 9-7B.

SPECIFICITY OF ENZYME ACTION

Specificity is perhaps the most characteristic property of the living machine. The enzyme-substrate relationship is an important example of this phenomenon. The *degree* of enzyme specificity varies to a certain extent.

Absolute specificity, as the name implies, means that the enzyme can catalyze the breakdown of only one substrate. The hydrolysis of urea by urease is an example of this. Any slight chemical modification of the urea molecule completely prevents it from being a substrate.

Absolute group specificity implies that the enzyme is capable of acting on a given organic group only. Thus alcohol dehydrogenases will act only on alcohols.

$$CH_3CH_2OH + \begin{array}{c}\text{oxidized}\\ \text{coenzyme}\end{array} \quad \underset{\rightleftarrows}{\overset{\begin{array}{c}\text{alcohol}\\ \text{dehydrogenase}\end{array}}{}} \quad CH_3CHO + \begin{array}{c}\text{reduced}\\ \text{coenzyme}\end{array}$$

In such cases the rate of enzyme activity will depend on the nature of the remaining portions of the molecule. In the case of alcohol dehydrogenases, the enzyme "prefers" ethanol but can act at decreasing rates on straight-chain alcohols of increasing lengths.

Relative group specificity refers to the property of enzymes that allows them to act on more than one organic group. Thus trypsin, which is able to split certain peptide bonds involving lysine or arginine residues, is also able to split their ester bonds.

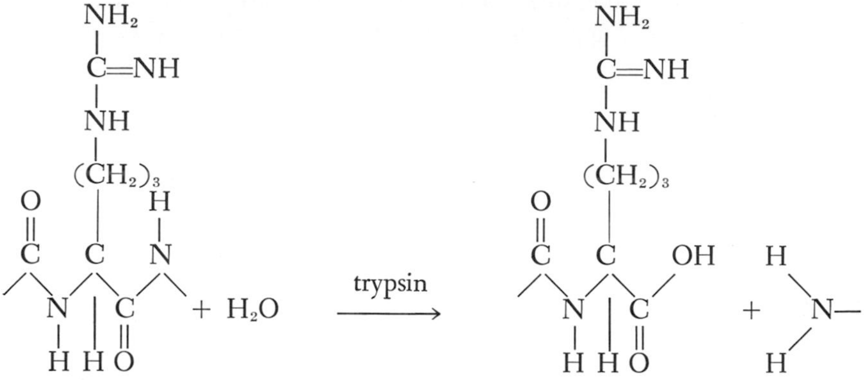

$$
\begin{array}{c}
NH_2 \\
| \\
C{=}NH \\
| \\
NH \\
| \\
(CH_2)_3
\end{array}
$$

arginine
residue

peptidase activity of trypsin

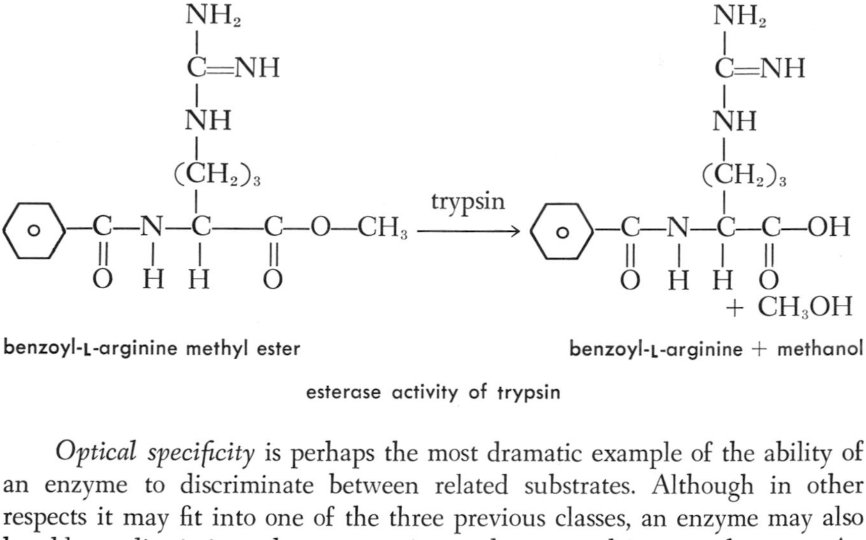

benzoyl-L-arginine methyl ester

benzoyl-L-arginine + methanol

esterase activity of trypsin

Optical specificity is perhaps the most dramatic example of the ability of an enzyme to discriminate between related substrates. Although in other respects it may fit into one of the three previous classes, an enzyme may also be able to discriminate between a given substrate and its *optical isomer*. An *l*-amino acid oxidase, for instance, will not act on *d*-amino acids and vice versa.

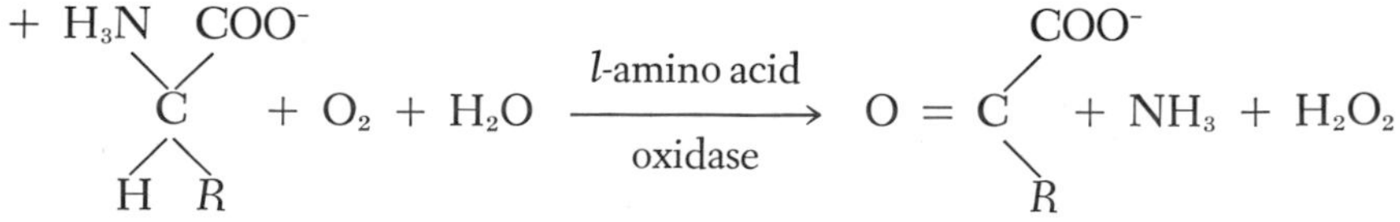

$$
\text{+ H}_3\text{N} \quad \text{COO}^- \qquad \qquad \qquad \qquad \text{COO}^-
$$

l-amino acid

α-keto acid

These and other numerous studies of enzyme specificity have provided us with certain insights into the mechanism of enzyme action. Before we are ready to discuss this important topic we must review an additional property of enzymes that is crucial to our understanding of enzyme action.

ENZYME INHIBITION

As we pointed out in Chapter 4, we can expect poisons to exert their biological effect on enzymes, for only through an inhibition of catalysis can we explain why poisons have such drastic effects at minute concentrations. Let us plot the Michaelis-Menten equation in a slightly different manner (Fig. 9-9). Note that by plotting $1/v$ against $1/[S]$ a straight line is obtained that intercepts the $1/v$ axis at $1/V$. This provides a convenient and

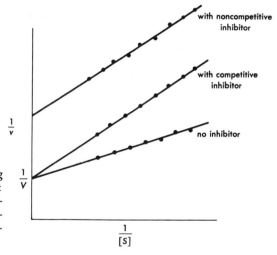

Fig. 9-9. Reciprocal plotting ($1/v$ versus $1/[S]$) gives straight lines which by extrapolation reveals difference between competitive and noncompetitive inhibition.

accurate means of estimating V. The slope turns out to be K_m/V and hence K_m can also be estimated quite conveniently. Fig. 9-9 shows that two types of enzyme inhibition can be distinguished. One of them, termed *noncompetitive*, is characterized by the fact that the action of the inhibitor on the enzyme is not modified by a change in substrate concentration. Thus at infinite substrate concentration one is still able to measure some enzyme inhibition; that is, the inhibited and noninhibited curves do not intersect at $1/[S] = 0$. Noncompetitive inhibition includes many chemical effects on the enzyme that have a direct or indirect effect on its activity. An example of this might be the covering up on the enzyme of one or more sulfhydryl groups that are required for enzyme action.

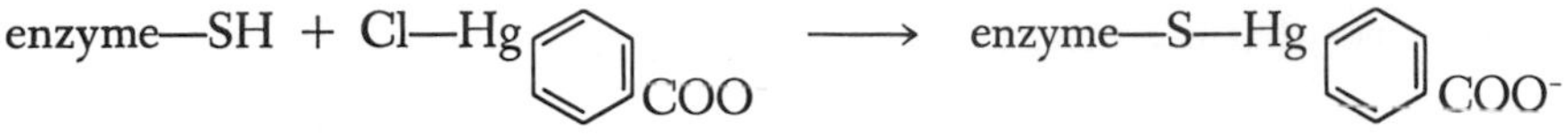

enzyme—SH + Cl—Hg ⟨benzene ring⟩ COO   ⟶   enzyme—S—Hg ⟨benzene ring⟩ COO⁻

p-chloromercuribenzoate

inhibited
enzyme

In *competitive inhibition* the effect of the inhibitor is reduced by increasing the substrate concentration. Here the inhibitory effect all but vanishes when the substrate concentration becomes infinite. Thus the two lines will intersect at $1/[S] = 0$. This behavior can be explained by assuming that the inhibitor competes reversibly with the substrate for a portion of the enzyme that is directly involved in the catalytic process. The effect of malonic acid as a competitive inhibitor of the oxidation of succinate acid is a classic example of competitive inhibition (see Chapter 11).

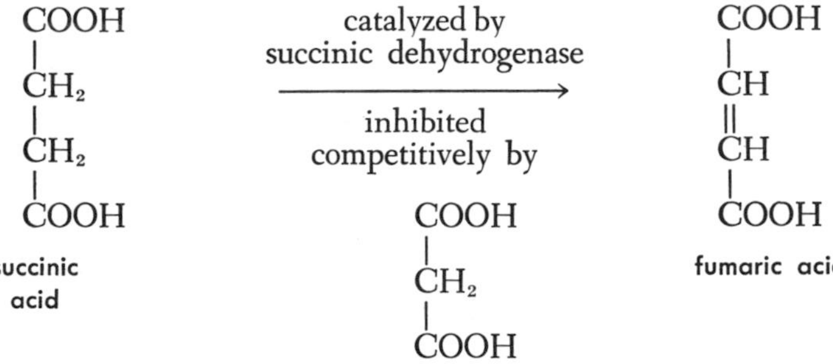

$$
\begin{array}{ccc}
\text{COOH} & \text{catalyzed by} & \text{COOH} \\
| & \text{succinic dehydrogenase} & | \\
\text{CH}_2 & \xrightarrow{\hspace{2cm}} & \text{CH} \\
| & \text{inhibited} & || \\
\text{CH}_2 & \text{competitively by} & \text{CH} \\
| & & | \\
\text{COOH} & \text{COOH} & \text{COOH} \\
\end{array}
$$

succinic
acid

COOH
|
CH₂
|
COOH

malonic acid

fumaric acid

The competitive inhibitor is sufficiently similar to the real substrate to form an inhibitor-enzyme complex, yet its difference from the substrate prevents the enzyme from acting catalytically on it. In the presence of an inhibitor some of the enzyme is "tied up" and cannot act catalytically, an effect that can be decreased by increasing the substrate concentration.

Another well-known example of this is the effect of sulfanilamide (a sulfa drug), which "fools" the enzyme normally acting on p-aminobenzoic acid, an important growth factor in many bacteria.

HO   O
  \\ //
   C
⟨benzene ring⟩
   NH₂

p-aminobenzoic acid

H₂N   O
   \\ //
O=S
⟨benzene ring⟩
   NH₂

sulfanilamide

Note again the general structural similarities between the two compounds.

MECHANISM OF ENZYME ACTION

The discussion thus far leads to the general conclusion that enzyme catalysis involves the close interaction of enzyme and substrate. The fact that structural changes of the enzyme molecule (denaturation) cause marked decreases in enzyme activity suggests that the enzyme requires a specific secondary, tertiary, and possibly quaternary structure for its catalytic property. The phenomenon of optical specificity suggests that at least in some cases three of the four substituents of the optically active carbon atom must be in contact with the enzyme surface (Fig. 9-10). A close relationship between enzyme and substrate is also suggested, even if somewhat indirectly, by the phenomenon of competitive inhibition.

This notion of a close relationship between a given region of the enzyme and certain groups of the substrate molecule has led to the concept of the *active site*. According to this concept there are one or more regions on the enzyme at which the catalytic transformations take place. What is the nature of the active site? Although work on the active site of enzymes has only just begun, there are a number of interesting observations that point in the direction in which we can expect progress to be made.

There are the so-called conjugated enzymes in which "prosthetic groups" are necessary for enzyme activity. Since we can expect the prosthetic group to be at least part of the active site of the enzyme, we have the opportunity to study the structural chemistry of this region. Wang carried out an interesting study on *catalase*, the enzyme catalyzing the decomposition of hydrogen peroxide into oxygen and water. Catalase has a prosthetic group com-

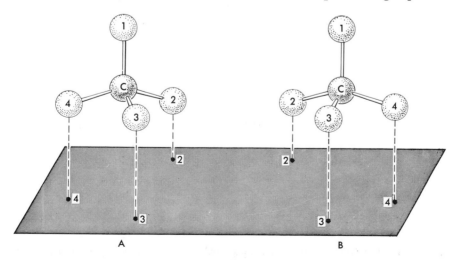

Fig. 9-10. Demonstration that optical specificity must be due to minimum of 3-point contact. Two-point contact cannot distinguish between the optical isomers A and B.

posed of an iron atom and a *heme group* (hematin). It is possible to measure the catalytic effects of the iron alone (weak) and of hematin (less weak); the conclusion, as might be expected, is that the protein portion of the enzyme does play a crucial role in catalysis (Fig. 9-11). It is very likely that the hematin group is located on the enzyme in such a manner that the substrate will interact with portions of the protein molecule as well as with the prosthetic group. An alternative hypothesis assumes that the interacion of the protein and the hematin modifies the properties of the latter in such a way as to increase its catalytic activity. Wang was able to synthesize a compound (ferric triethylenetetraamine) that is a much more effective catalyst than hematin but is still far less effective than the enzyme (Fig. 9-11). By placing the NH_2 groups close to the iron this compound possibly simulates the situation of the iron in the hematin-protein complex of catalase. Such studies of the catalytic activity of enzyme analogues are likely to be of increasing importance in the immediate future.

Another approach that has recently yielded some interesting results is to remove portions of the enzyme molecule by selectively splitting specific pep-

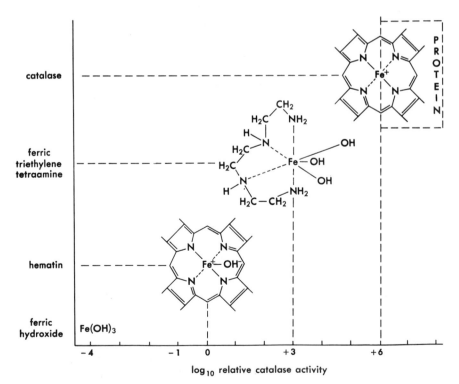

Fig. 9-11. Catalytic activity exerted by a number of compounds on the decomposition of hydrogen peroxide. (Courtesy of J. H. Wang.)

tide bonds with certain proteolytic (protein-splitting) enzymes. Emil Smith and his colleagues have succeeded in removing more than 100 amino acid residues from the 185 found in the enzyme *papain* without abolishing activity. F. M. Richards, using the action of the enzyme subtilisin on the enzyme ribonuclease, was able to split off a 20-residue peptide. It was possible to abolish ribonuclease activity by removing this peptide and to regenerate enzyme activity by adding it. Studies such as these will provide an increasingly precise picture of the portion of the enzyme required for catalytic activity.

An approach that has come back into use in recent years is the specific blocking of R groups on the enzyme molecule. It has been known for a long time that certain enzymes require for their activity the presence of one or more specific sulfhydryl groups. When such groups become tied up by a mercurial reagent like *p*-chloromercuribenzoate, or an alkylating reagent like iodoacetamide, then enzyme activity is lost.

$$\text{enzyme}-\text{SH} + \text{I}-\underset{\underset{\text{H}}{|}}{\overset{\overset{\text{H}}{|}}{\text{C}}}-\underset{\text{O}}{\overset{\text{NH}_2}{\text{C}}} \longrightarrow \overset{\text{inhibited}}{\underset{\text{enzyme}}{}} -\text{S}-\underset{\underset{\text{H}}{|}}{\overset{\overset{\text{H}}{|}}{\text{C}}}-\underset{\text{O}}{\overset{\text{NH}_2}{\text{C}}} + \text{HI}$$

iodoacetamide

Recent work on a number of enzymes has implicated some additional groups like histidine, aspartic acid, tyrosine, and serine; and we can expect this list to grow rapidly in the immediate future. Perhaps the most exciting example of such work has been in connection with certain R groups that turned out to be unusually reactive. In the case of ribonuclease, Barnard and Stein discovered that a histidine R group located in the 119 position (Fig. 8-13) is unusually reactive toward bromoacetic acid. This reagent does not react as readily with the other three histidines in the molecule nor does it react readily with histidine in solution. Furthermore—and this is most significant—the special reactivity of histidine 119 is lost if ribonuclease is denatured, since it is dependent on the specific configuration of the native enzyme.

The picture of biocatalysis that emerges involves a close structural relationship between the enzyme and the substrate. The specific surface or site on the enzyme where the temporary union takes place is presumably composed of R groups brought into rigid juxtaposition by the coiling, folding, and associating of the secondary, tertiary, and quaternary structures of the enzyme respectively. It is expected that the juxtaposition of these groups modifies their reactivity in certain ways so as to make the active site not only specific in its spatial configuration but also very special in its chemical reactivity. A substrate that becomes temporarily clasped at the active site is brought under strain and hence activated. Such, at any rate, is the present, somewhat vague, state of our thinking.

The precise mechanism by which an enzyme lowers the activation energy necessary for a given reaction is still to be discovered. Nevertheless, the general direction of the search has become clear. We must get to know the three-dimensional structural chemistry of the active site and possibly of the whole enzyme. With the new developments in x-ray crystallography and the increasing precision of other techniques of structural analysis, we can safely say that this goal is within sight.

SUGGESTED READING LIST

BALDWIN, E., 1957. *Dynamic aspects of biochemistry*, 3d ed. Cambridge: Cambridge University Press.

BOYER, P. D., LARDY, H., and MYRBACK, K., 1959. *The enzymes.* New York: Academic Press.

COLOWICK, S. P., and KAPLAN, N. O., 1955. *Methods in enzymology.* New York: Academic Press.

FRUTON, J. S., and SIMMONDS, S., 1958. *General biochemistry*, 2d ed. New York: Wiley.

MEHLER, A. H., 1957. *Introduction to enzymology.* New York: Academic Press.

NEILANDS, J. B., and STUMPF, P. K., 1958. *Outlines of enzyme chemistry*, 2d ed. New York: Wiley.

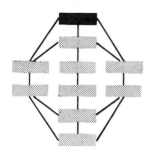

CHAPTER TEN

METABOLIC

PATHWAYS
Thus far we have discussed enzymes and how they act on substrates either to oxidize or reduce them, to split them with water or with phosphate, or to combine two smaller molecules to make a larger molecule. But what are these substrates, these compounds acted upon by enzymes? Primarily they are the foodstuffs taken in by cells, or the breakdown products of these foodstuffs. For example, whatever we take into our own bodies, be it carbohydrate, fat, protein, nucleic acids, or various other constituents, is broken down into smaller molecules by enzymes in the saliva and in the gastrointestinal tract. The breakdown products then enter the various cells of the body, via the blood stream, through mechanisms detailed in Chapter 15. In some cells breakdown proceeds still further; in some other cells occurs the synthesis of larger molecules from the smaller ones; in yet others the predominant mode of attack may be various transformations of these compounds. In most cases, the various cells of the body can perform all of these functions. All in all, the preponderant mode of utilization or metabolism of these compounds in the various cells of different organs varies according to the nature of the cells. Some, like the liver cell, are very active in providing a good deal of the circulating proteins of the blood and in mobilizing glucose for the use of the rest of the cells, mostly the muscle cells, of the body. Other cells, like the various secretory cells of the different glands, are active in synthesizing and secreting hormones, which, via the blood, are then deposited at their respective end-organ sites, and are then active in some aspects in regulating the over-all metabolism of the body. In these tasks, and in many others that will be outlined in later chapters, the cell does work, and in doing work, it requires the expenditure of energy. In general it obtains energy by metabolizing a portion of the same breakdown products that are used in the synthesis of the larger compounds of the cell. Thus, some of the breakdown products are used to synthesize glucose, or glycogen, in liver and muscle cells, while some of the rest is metabolized to provide the energy for these syntheses.

In Carbohydrate Metabolism

From this bare outline it is clear that many of the substrates, or metabolites, are attacked not just in one way, by a single enzyme. In many cases, there is more than one enzyme attacking the same metabolite—one to oxidize it, one to reduce it, and one to attach some other compound to it. We can thus speak of *metabolic pathways*, that is, the various directions a metabolite can go. The same substance, for example, can be attacked by one enzyme to produce chemical energy and can also be put by another enzyme onto the pathway for the synthesis of some of the larger molecules of the cell, as proteins and nucleic acids. A good example is the fate of glucose-6-phosphate in the liver cell (Fig. 10-1). It can be formed in various enzymatic ways, as from glycogen, or from smaller intermediates of fermentation, or from free glucose (see Chapter 14). Once it is formed it can be acted upon by four different enzymes; that is, there are four vectors to its metabolism: (1) to replenish the supply of glucose in the blood, (2) to build up liver glycogen as a storehouse for blood and muscle cell glucose, (3) to provide intermediates for the syntheses of fats, proteins, and nucleic acids, and (4) to provide energy.

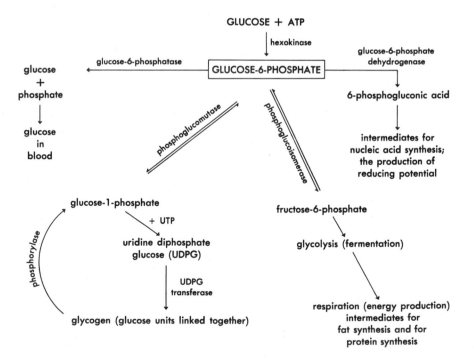

Fig. 10-1. General pathway for glucose in liver cell.

How exactly all this is regulated by the liver cell we do not know, but it is almost certain that the relative rates of the enzymatic reactions and various hormones have a hand in this regulation, by determining what proportion of the glucose molecules travel along each route. Nature is conservative, in the sense that the same compound acts as a starting point for many different metabolic pathways. We can guess that the reason is because regulation of the over-all metabolism—the physiology—of the cell is much easier if there are fewer key points that must be accommodated. The switch from one pathway to another becomes then more responsive to the needs of the cell. In the example given above the key compound might be glucose-6-phosphate. Also, although the example is the liver cell, other cells, as distant biologically as the yeast cell, have most of the same enzymes, have the same pathways, and are probably prone to the same sort of regulation.

However, even the simplified diagram of Fig. 10-1 does not give all the other known alternative pathways in this large subfield of metabolism. For example, the synthesis of nucleic acids is a necessary requisite of cell growth, as later chapters will point out. One of the constituents of these complicated compounds is the 5-carbon sugar, ribose. The immediate precursor of ribose, ribose-5-phosphate, is synthesized via many pathways. From the carbohydrate precursor, glucose-6-phosphate, there are actually three pathways leading to the formation of this compound (Fig. 10-2). One of these, the pentose phosphate pathway, has been known for a long time. Actually, two pentose phosphate pathways are now recognized, the oxidative and nonoxidative. The former, leading to ribose-5-phosphate in four enzymatic steps, is a prime source of reducing potential in the form of $NADPH_2$ (see below); reducing potential because this coenzyme, $NADPH_2$, is a necessary concomitant reactant for the syntheses of fatty acids and steroids. The nonoxidative pentose phosphate pathway begins with the conversion of glucose-6-phosphate to fructose-6-phosphate. But instead of continuing on this glycolytic road (see Fig. 14-2), the carbon atoms of fructose-6-phosphate go through a series of condensation and transfer reactions, leading, via the important enzymes transaldolase and transketolase, to xylulose-5-phosphate and ribose-5-phosphate. The former compound is also made via the oxidative pathway and via another road, called the uronic acid pathway, by way of uridine diphosphate glucose and 11 enzymatic reactions. Since xylulose-5-phosphate can be converted to ribose-5-phosphate via the intermediacy of ribulose-5-phosphate, the uronic acid pathway is also a source of the ribose moiety of nucleic acids.

Radioactive tracers indicate that all these pathways seem to be operating in the cell at the same time, though the traffic on the road leading to ribose via the uronic acids seems to be insignificant compared to the other two. In the liver and muscle cells at least, the uridine diphosphate glucose formed thereby is funneled off into glycogen synthesis. But why should these multitudinous sources of ribose exist? We are not sure, but we think that since

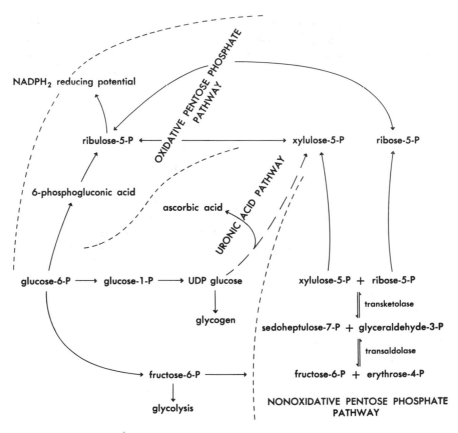

Fig. 10-2. Pentose phosphate pathways.

nucleic acid synthesis is necessary for the cell to grow or even to exist, the cell has provided itself with more than one pathway for its synthesis in case the others are blocked out. This can be illustrated experimentally by making use of the observation that the vitamin thiamine, in the form of thiamine pyrophosphate, is a necessary cofactor in the functioning of the nonoxidative pathway enzymes transaldolase and transketolase. In normal animals, it was demonstrated that, of all the carbon atoms of glucose going to ribose, about 40 percent of the radioactive carbon atoms of administered glucose was converted to ribose carbon atoms by the oxidative pathway and 60 percent by the nonoxidative pathway. However, in animals rendered thiamine deficient, about 80 percent of the ribose carbons were formed via the oxidative pathway. Thus the cell seems to have evolved multiple pathways to make certain that a necessary compound is formed no matter under what environmental conditions the cell might find itself. In the above case, this compound is ribose-5-phosphate. Another example involving the same alternative pathways could be the need of the cell to make enough $NADPH_2$ for the synthesis of steroids and fats.

THE KREBS CYCLE; ITS MEANING

This conservatism of nature is shown too in the fact that almost the same pathway exists for the synthesis of large molecules and for the production of energy. This is not entirely true for the entire length of the pathway, for it is now known that there are different portions of the pathway for the breakdown and synthesis of proteins, for the breakdown and synthesis of carbohydrates (see Chapter 14), and for the breakdown and synthesis of fats. But lower down on the metabolic ladder, where the intermediates for all these processes lie, the metabolic pathways are so arranged that a change in direction, so to speak, can lead either to the combustion of an intermediate to provide energy or to the coupling of an intermediate with another compound to give larger molecules. In this sense the biochemist speaks of cycles, of true wheels. Perhaps it is easiest to explain this by going into the details of the most famous and oldest of these cycles, the tricarboxylic acid (TCA) cycle, or Krebs cycle, named for its formulator. In doing so, we will also learn a bit of how a biochemist works and how these pathways came to be formulated. It is a fascinating story.

The cycle is shown in Fig. 10-3. Essentially, it is a scheme by which the two carbon atoms of acetic acid are oxidized to carbon dioxide and water, and at the same time a great deal of biological energy is produced. This 2-carbon compound is actually acetyl coenzyme A, and its production is a result of the previous breakdown of fat and carbohydrate foodstuffs. Carbohydrate, when taken into the body of a multicellular organism, is in the form of large polymers of glucose units that must first be broken down to smaller units. The breaking down into single glucose molecules is done by mainly extracellular enzymes, enzymes that are secreted by cells. Glucose then enters the cells of the body by means that will be outlined later. In the case of single-celled organisms like bacteria and some fungi, the carbohydrate in the environment is broken down either by enzymes secreted into the medium by the cells or by enzymes situated on the surface of the cells. The glucose now inside is then broken down by a series of enzymes known collectively as the glycolytic enzymes (see Chapter 14). The end product of all this is usually pyruvic acid. This compound in turn is oxidized to acetyl coenzyme A in a very complicated enzymatic reaction. The latter compound can either become further oxidized via the TCA cycle, or it can go through a series of reactions in which it successively condenses with itself or with a derivative of itself to form the higher fatty acids. These fatty acids are straight-chain compounds,

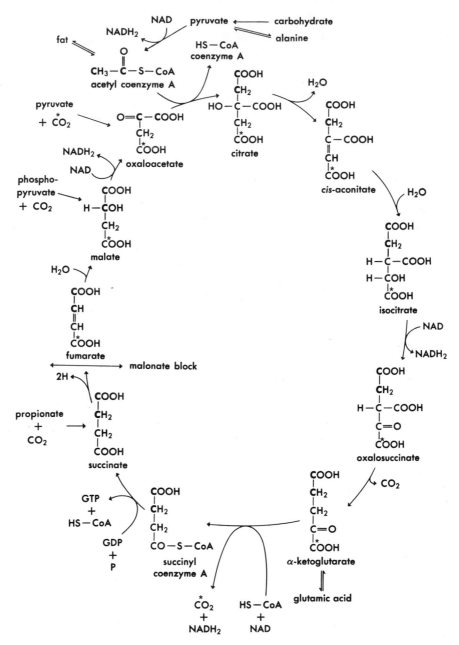

Fig. 10-3. Tricarboxylic acid (Krebs) cycle.

14 to 20 carbon atoms long. This is how carbohydrate becomes converted to fat, and how sugar eaten ends up as body fat.

Why in some circumstances the acetyl coenzyme A gets oxidized to provide energy, and in other instances it condenses to form longer fatty acids to provide fats, we do not know, but there are some possible explanations based on the circumstances of the TCA cycle. For example, note that in Fig. 10-3 the first step in the oxidation of acetyl coenzyme A is the condensation, with the aid of an enzyme called simply "condensing enzyme," of this compound with oxaloacetate, forming citrate. Now suppose there were very little oxaloacetate available for this step. The condensation would be much reduced in amount, and acetyl coenzyme A could not be further oxidized in large amounts; instead, a good deal of it would go onto an alternate pathway. The latter pathway is the one enabling acetyl coenzyme A to form long-chain fatty acid. The shunting at this point is one of the possible ways a common precursor is transformed into either carbohydrate or fat.

To get back to the cycle, the citrate formed in the above reaction is attacked by an enzyme, aconitase, that causes an equilibrium to be established between three compounds, citrate, cis-aconitate, and isocitrate. The direction of reaction is constantly being shifted toward isocitrate formation, because there exists an enzyme that attacks isocitrate; by removing isocitrate from the reaction with aconitase, the overall equilibrium results in the formation of more isocitrate from cis-aconitate and citrate. This kind of an event, the shifting of one enzymatic equilibrium by means of another enzymatic attack on one of the compounds involved, is not a singular occurrence in the cell, but goes on constantly. In this way many reactions that are thermodynamically reversible, in which very little change in free energy is involved, are constantly being rendered "enzymatically" irreversible—that is, caused to go most of the way in one direction. If the concentration of isocitrate is increased, as can be done experimentally, formation of citrate from isocitrate will result.

The enzyme that attacks isocitrate, called isocitrate dehydrogenase, uses nicotinamide-adenine-dinucleotide (NAD) as a coenzyme, whereas a similar enzyme uses nicotinamide-adenine-dinucleotide phosphate (NADP). These two coenzymes were formerly known as diphosphopyridine nucleotide (DPN) and triphosphopyridine nucleotide (TPN). In the process, isocitrate is oxidized to oxalosuccinate, with the loss of two hydrogen atoms, giving $NADH_2$, or reduced NAD (and in the other case, $NADPH_2$). The same enzyme, probably at the same time, causes a decarboxylation of oxalosuccinate, giving α-ketoglutarate and carbon dioxide. The carbon dioxide comes from the oxidation of one of the carbon atoms of the original oxaloacetate. The formation of $NADH_2$ is notable in that its subsequent oxidation leads to a production of biological energy. How the latter process is accomplished will be discussed in the next chapter. It suffices here to point out this further function of the cycle, the originating of the production of most of the usable energy of the cell.

The next step, the oxidative decarboxylation of α-ketoglutarate to form succinate and carbon dioxide, by means of the enzyme α-ketoglutarate dehydrogenase, is also a very complicated reaction. Coenzyme A again takes part, and what is actually obtained is not succinate but succinyl coenzyme A. This dehydrogenation takes place again with the aid of NAD, forming $NADH_2$, and again this $NADH_2$ is further oxidized to provide energy. There is also, however, another step in this over-all reaction that provides energy. This is the enzymatic removal of coenzyme A from succinyl coenzyme A, with the aid of guanosine diphosphate (GDP) and inorganic phosphate, to form guanosine triphosphate (GTP). This GTP is a high-energy compound, the properties of which were mentioned earlier. Thus the whole sequence of reactions from α-ketoglutarate to succinate provides for energy production, in the formation of $NADH_2$ and GTP. This GTP can enzymatically react with adenosine diphosphate (ADP) to form GDP and adenosine triphosphate (ATP). It is the latter nucleotide, ATP, that has been called the energy coin of the biological realm. Notice, incidentally, that during the oxidation of α-ketoglutarate another molecule of carbon dioxide is removed from the original oxaloacetate.

The next reaction, succinic dehydrogenation, is a very powerful one, in which two hydrogen atoms are removed from succinate, and fumarate is formed. In the process, the two hydrogen atoms, left dangling in the scheme, are transferred to cytochrome b, to form reduced cytochrome b. This cytochrome b is an electron carrier protein containing an iron heme as a prosthetic group; we will have more to say about this type of compound in the next chapter.

The fumarate resulting from the above reaction then takes on a molecule of water, with the aid of the enzyme fumarase, to form malate. Malate is oxidized by malic dehydrogenase and NAD, forming $NADH_2$ and oxaloacetate again. By following the two carbon atoms (bold-face type) of acetate throughout the cycle, you will notice that they end up in the new oxaloacetate molecule. Thus, although oxaloacetate is back again, it is not precisely the same molecule, since it has lost carbon atoms as carbon dioxide and has regained them from the acetyl coenzyme A. This oxaloacetate molecule can now accept another molecule of acetyl coenzyme A and the cycle will be repeated. We can say, then, that the two carbon dioxide molecules result from the oxidation of acetate.

The cycle is the key to the oxidation of fats and carbohydrates, for we now know that most of the fat and a good deal of the carbohydrate is oxidized via the cycle. Since α-ketoglutaric, oxaloacetic, and pyruvic acids can be formed very easily from the amino acids glutamic and aspartic acids and alanine, the cycle is also responsible for the oxidation of some of the protein intermediates of the cell. This view is strengthened by the fact that many of the other amino acids can be broken down to intermediates such as acetyl coenzyme A, α-ketoglutarate, oxaloacetate, succinate, or fumarate. It can be estimated that the oxidation of the carbon atoms of most of the substrates taken in by the cell proceeds through this cycle. This happens in all kinds of cells, from most of the different kinds of cells in our body to plant cells to yeast and bacterial cells.

What about the reverse of this coin? The cycle is also involved in the syntheses of intermediates leading to the formation of larger molecules. For example, by amination, the putting in of ammonia in various ways, many amino acids are formed from the intermediates of the cycle. In turn, some of the amino acids are precursors of purines and pyrimidines, thus of nucleic acids, and also are the precursors of porphyrins. Oxaloacetate, the initial condensant in the cycle, is also on the pathway for the syntheses of hexose and pentose, the latter being involved as the sugar moiety of the nucleic acids. In ancillary reactions to the cycle, as given in the scheme, carbon dioxide can be fixed into organic form, combining with pyruvate to form oxaloacetate, with phosphopyruvate to form malate, and with propionate to form succinate. These reactions bring carbon dioxide into the scheme to form cellular substance. This use of carbon dioxide is found not only in photosynthesis, via different reactions, but also, to some extent via the above reactions, in our own "plantlike" bodies. Even from this very brief survey, it can be seen that the cycle has a central role in the metabolism of foodstuffs by cells. Through it pass most of the chemical intermediates—most of the carbon atoms, to be exact—of the chemical constituents of the cell. It is the hub of a great many of the pathways involved in the breakdown and synthesis of cellular constituents. The reason this is so is that the intermediates of the cycle, particularly the 4-carbon ones, are very much involved as intermediates in other pathways of the chemical metabolism of the cell. Sooner or later, the compounds involved in the latter pathways reach some part of the cycle. When this happens, their carbon atoms can either be oxidized, to provide energy, or can be shunted onto another pathway.

Although the framework of the cycle has been well established, very little is known of how carbon atoms are shunted about, of how the cycle "knows" which way to function—that is, whether as a biological energy source, or as a mechanism for the syntheses of needed cell constituents, or as a means by which metabolism is shifted from one major pathway to another, say from carbohydrate to fat. From physiologic studies, we do know that these shifts can and do occur. Carbohydrate carbons do end up in fat; carbohydrate is made from smaller molecules and held in storage; carbohydrate is broken down to provide energy. Fat is synthesized or broken down; proteins are made or broken down. Carbohydrate, fat, and protein carbons are all interchangeable. All these events take place at one time or another. And because we now know most of the metabolic pathways along which these intermediates travel, we realize that the key place where the regulation of these pathways occurs is at the Krebs cycle.

What are the possible alternative pathways? A look at the cycle suggests several possibilities almost immediately, and experiments can be set up with minced tissues (homogenates) to test several of them. For example, pyruvate can be oxidized to carbon dioxide and water by these homogenates, via the Krebs cycle; for this to occur, however, it is necessary to add an adequate supply of 4-carbon acids, as oxaloacetic, or malic or fumaric, for all are interconvertible. If any of these 4-carbon acids are omitted from the reaction mixture, pyruvate is not oxidized, but instead is converted, via acetyl coenzyme A, to acetoacetate, one of the intermediate products of fat metabolism. This result shows that the acetyl coenzyme A did not condense with oxaloacetate to form citrate, but instead, condensed with itself to form acetoacetate. One can also add ammonium chloride, which, too, largely prevents the oxidation of pyruvate and causes it to be converted to acetoacetate. The reason probably is that the added ammonium chloride drains away the intermediates of the Krebs cycle, like α-ketoglutarate and oxaloacetate, causing them to be converted to the amino acids glutamate and aspartate. Since all the intermediates are in equilibrium with each other, a decrease in some will be reflected in a decrease in all, and thus the levels of intermediates will be too low to perform effective condensation with the acetyl coenzyme A derived from the pyruvate. Thus again, two of the carbon atoms of the pyruvate will end up as fat carbons.

Verification of the Cycle

But how do we know that something like this actually happens within the whole cell or within the animal? We do not know precisely, but we can make fairly good guesses. Radioactive tracers such as carbon-14 can be incorporated into certain chemical compounds, as pyruvic acid, and the labeled pyruvic acid then given to the whole organism, be it a yeast cell or a rat. Various chemical compounds—glucose, fat, and amino acids—are then isolated. By knowing which carbon atom of the pyruvic acid was labeled, and by determining which carbon atoms of the isolated compounds are labeled, we can infer pretty well, knowing the individual biochemical reactions involved, what happened in the organism to the individual carbon atoms of the ingested pyruvic acid. On the basis of many such experiments, many investigators have come to the inescapable conclusions that the Krebs cycle is operative in the cell, as well as in the test tube; that there are alternative metabolic pathways for many of the intermediates of fat, carbohydrate, and amino acid metabolism; and that these intermediates intersect each other at the level of the Krebs cycle. The reactions of the Krebs cycle can explain fully the means whereby the carbon atoms of pyruvate end up in various other compounds. In science, this verifiable predictability is considered to be proof of the present-day "truth" of the theory.

This brings us to the original evidence for the cycle and the grounds on which Krebs formulated the scheme. In minced tissue, like breast muscle or liver, it was very early noticed that the addition of only very small amounts of citrate catalyzed a large respiration. It was also found that citrate could be synthesized when oxaloacetate was added, and that citrate, isocitrate, cis-aconitate, and α-ketoglutarate were all rapidly oxidized by these minced tissues. But the key finding in the early laboratory work involved the use of a particular enzyme inhibitor, malonic acid, which specifically inhibits the enzyme succinic dehydrogenase and prevents the interchange of hydrogens between succinate and fumarate. However, it was noticed that even in the presence of malonate, succinate could actually be synthesized when fumarate or oxaloacetate was added. By looking at the cycle, we can see that succinate could not have been formed by the direct reduction of fumarate, for this enzyme was blocked by malonate. Krebs deduced that there must be a "back" reaction, by which succinate could be formed via the breakdown of α-ketoglutarate. Thus a cycle was postulated, using the tricarboxylic acids, citrate, isocitrate, and cis-aconitate, and the dicarboxylic acids, succinate, fumarate, malate, and oxaloacetate. Furthermore, in liver cells, in which carbon dioxide fixation can take place (via the reaction of pyruvate plus carbon dioxide giving oxaloacetate), citrate and α-ketoglutarate could be formed from pyruvate.

The next piece of evidence involved the use of radioactive carbon dioxide. When this compound was incubated with liver mince in the presence of pyruvate and malonate, it was found that the isolated succinate contained no radioactivity, and that the radioactivity in the isolated α-ketoglutarate was in the carboxyl carbon next to the carbonyl group. In Fig. 10-3, the radioactive carbon dioxide is marked with an asterisk; note that the radioactive label is found in oxaloacetate. Because of the block by malonate, the cycle has to go around "clockwise," and thus the label is found in citrate, cis-aconitate, isocitrate, oxalosuccinate, and α-ketoglutarate; it is not in succinate, however, because the labeled carboxyl group of α-ketoglutarate was removed by α-ketoglutarate dehydrogenase. If you look closely at the cycle, you might ask whether radioactivity was found in fumarate and malate, coming from radioactive oxaloacetate. There was, and since no radioactivity was present in succinate, it is apparent that the succinate did not arise from fumarate but must have been formed via a back reaction. When malonate was omitted, all the dicarboxylic acids, including succinate, contained radioactivity, showing the interconvertibility of the compounds in question. Also, because malonate specifically blocks succinate oxidation, it can be used as a test system for any compound that will form succinate in the presence of the inhibitor, since succinate actually accumulates under these conditions and can be extracted and its amount estimated. It was found that all of the intermediates of the Krebs cycle, as postulated, can form succinate under these conditions.

These pieces of evidence are explicable only by the reactions of the cycle. We could go on; for example, it was found that citrate could be formed from acetoacetate and oxaloacetate. Again, when radioactive acetate or acetoacetate was added to kidney minces, radioactive α-ketoglutarate was formed, and when radioactive acetate was injected into the whole animal, radioactive aspartic and glutamic acids were formed. Since the latter two amino acids are in equilibrium with oxaloacetate and α-ketoglutarate, we are sure that the cycle does function in the whole animal. A great deal of such evidence has been accumulated, from both test tube and whole-body experiments. The inescapable conclusion is that there is indeed such a thing as the Krebs cycle in the many cells of the mammalian body, as well as in most other cells of the plant and animal kingdoms. Perhaps the most telling bit of evidence has been the isolation and purification of all of the enzymes involved in the cycle, indicating that there are specific enzymes catalyzing these specific reactions. That the cycle is important for the economy of the cell is illustrated by the finding that the ingestion of fluoroacetate can kill an animal; this poison stops the cycle by inhibiting the enzyme aconitase, concomitantly piling up fluorocitrate in the cell.

The Krebs cycle, then, is a complex metabolic relationship between many of the intermediates of the large classes of foodstuffs taken in by the organism. It is a means whereby all these intermediates can be somewhat interchanged; whereby, for example, the energy in carbohydrate can be stored for future use in the form of fat, and the protein stores of the body, mostly in muscle, can be changed to fat and carbohydrate and used for energy. The cycle has another equally important function, namely, the transformation of chemical energy into the energy the cell needs to perform its various functions; this is the subject of Chapter 11.

GLYOXALATE CYCLE

The Krebs cycle is only one of a number of what we call intersecting pathways of metabolism. It is the rare chemical compound that is metabolized along only a single metabolic sequence. Even the Krebs cycle itself is only a central hub of impinging pathways. For example, it has been long noted that the growth of many bacteria and fungi can be sustained by the addition to the medium of simple 2-carbon compounds like acetate. Acetate in these organisms, unlike the case in mammals, can give rise to a net increase in carbohydrate and protein via the glyoxalate cycle (Fig. 10-4).

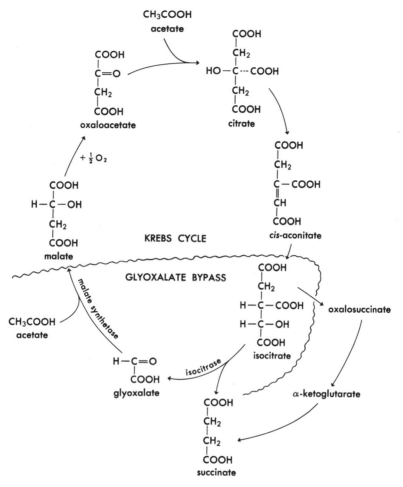

Fig. 10-4. Interaction between the Krebs cycle and the glyoxalate bypass.

The cycle can be seen to intersect the Krebs cycle at the malic and isocitric acid levels. The bacteria and fungi have at this point two enzymes not found in animals: isocitrase, which splits isocitrate to glyoxalate and succinate; and malate synthetase, which condenses the glyoxalate with another molecule of acetate to form malate. Thus, over all, two moles of acetate are converted to one mole of succinate. The succinate can of course enter the Krebs cycle and thereby become a source of carbohydrate and protein carbon atoms. Thus the difference between the Krebs cycle and what might be called its glyoxalate cycle bypath is that acetate carbons are oxidized by the former whereas they are converted to oxaloacetate and hence to carbohydrate and protein by the latter. It is intriguing to speculate about the control mechanisms that determine whether isocitrase or isocitric dehydrogenase acts; this is the key point, the intersection between these two cycles. At present we can only speculate; we have no answers.

A Case Study

Finally, the case of methionine metabolism (Fig. 10-5) will illustrate once again the manifold roles in which a single molecule can masquerade. Methionine is an amino acid constituent of proteins. Because of its labile methyl group (CH_3), it acts as a methylating agent; it can methylate, or transfer its methyl groups to methyl acceptors to form such compounds as choline and creatine. The former is important in that it is a constituent of the phospholipids forming the internal and external membranes of the cell (see Chapter 15), and it is also a key factor in lipid metabolism. Creatine, as phosphocreatine, is an energy source in muscle (Chapter 14). These involvements of methionine can be illustrated by injecting ethionine into an animal. Various physiological disorders ensue, particularly to liver and pancreas; derangements in protein, nucleic acid, and phospholipid metabolism occur. Ethionine is a metabolic antagonist of methionine; it differs from methionine only in having a —S—CH_2CH_3 group instead of a —S—CH_3

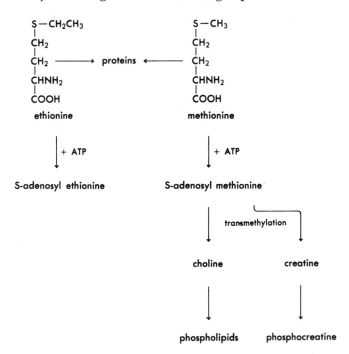

Fig. 10-5 Ethionine, a metabolic antagonist.

group, and thus it can replace methionine in many metabolic reactions. It acts like methionine in that it becomes attached to other amino acids by peptide bonds and becomes incorporated into proteins; some of these proteins, because of this replacement, are thus rendered unsatisfactory for their metabolic roles. Ethionine also competes with methionine for various enzymatic reactions that require methionine. Methionine is "activated" for methyl group transfer by reacting with ATP, the high-energy compound, forming the "active" methionine compound, S-adenosyl methionine. Likewise, ethionine is attacked by the same enzyme, but converted to S-adenosyl ethionine. However, the latter compound is not, like S-adenosyl methionine, a substrate for the various methyl-group transferring enzymes, and hence it is a dead end. If enough ethionine gets into a cell that has the methionine-activating enzyme, it can drain off the ATP of the cell into its cul-de-sac; hence both nucleic acid metabolism and energy metabolism are interfered with. All these multiple events take place when a cell ingests this simple, single metabolic antagonist. This observation is a fitting ending to the recital of the metabolic schemes of a cell in which one compound enjoys not one, but many functions. The cell is conservative, harboring its substance, hoarding its energy.

We now know of the existence of many enzymes, of many enzymatic pathways, involving the small molecules of the cell. "Metabolic maps" have even been published in book form, listing the actions and interactions between substrates and enzymes along these pathways, involving not only carbohydrate, but protein, fat, and nucleic acid precursors. Although this mapping has not been an easy task, requiring as it has years of work on the part of hundreds of individuals, it is still much easier than the formidable task still ahead: the understanding of the regulations along these pathways, of the means whereby a cell determines which roads are chosen in order that the final destinations will have some benefit to the economy of the cell as a whole. We must not forget that the cell is an integrated metabolic entity, not merely a collection of spatially and temporally separated enzymatic reactions. Some of the ideas that are currently held as to the nature of metabolic control mechanisms will be outlined in Chapter 16.

SUGGESTED READING LIST

AXELROD, BERNARD, "Glycolysis." In Greenberg, D. M. (ed.), 1960. *Metabolic pathways*. New York: Academic Press. Vol. 1, p. 97.
GREEN, DAVID E., "The synthesis of fat," *Scientific American*, February 1960.
———, "The metabolism of fats," *Scientific American*, January 1954.
———, "Enzymes in teams," *Scientific American*, September 1949.

GREENBERG, D. M. (ed.), 1960. *Metabolic pathways.* New York: Academic Press. Vols. 1 and 2, chapters on fat and amino acid metabolism.

KREBS, HANS A., and LOWENSTEIN, JOHN M., "The tricarboxylic acid cycle." In Greenberg, D. M. (ed.), 1960. *Metabolic pathways.* New York: Academic Press. Vol. 1, p. 129.

McELROY, W. D., 1961. *Cellular physiology and biochemistry.* Englewood Cliffs, N.J.: Prentice-Hall.

POTTER, VAN R., and HEIDELBERGER, CHARLES, "Alternative metabolic pathways," *Physiological Reviews,* Vol. 30 (1950), p. 505.

WOOD, HARLAND G., "Significance of alternate pathways in metabolism of glucose," *Physiological Reviews,* Vol. 35 (1955), p. 841.

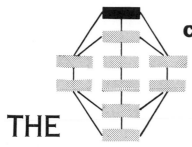

CHAPTER ELEVEN

THE

MITOCHONDRION

AND THE

FIXATION

OF ENERGY
Cells are energy converters; they are necessarily so because they need energy to perform their numerous tasks. To survive and to divide, to bring in substrates from the environment, to move about, to contract, and to expand—all the activities of various cells, be it mechanical work, osmotic work, or the concentrating of various solutes, require energy. Finally, the synthesizing of compounds in order to make new cells requires work. The importance of mitochondria lies precisely in the fact that they supply practically all of the necessary biological energy, and they do so primarily by oxidizing the substrates of the Krebs cycle. A cell gets its energy from the enzymatic oxidation of chemical compounds, and in this chapter we will describe what is known about this process.

MITOCHONDRIA: HISTORY AND DESCRIPTION

In the 1920's Warburg, an innovator in biochemistry, found that the oxidative reactions that take place in most tissues were concentrated in a small part of the cells. By grinding up the tissue he made what we now call a homogenate of the tissue; we now do it with a revolving pestle that fits snugly inside a glass tube into which the tissue and a suitable medium have

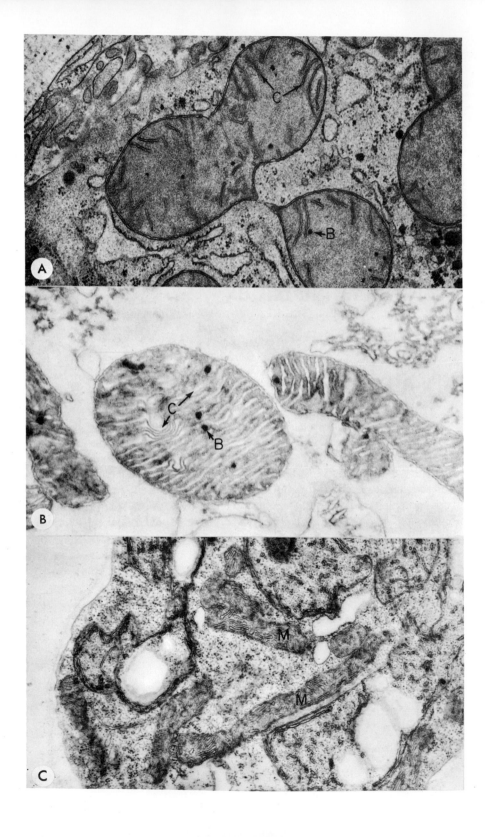

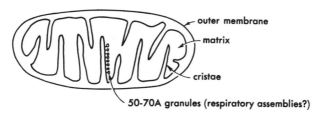

outer membrane

matrix

cristae

50-70A granules (respiratory assemblies?)

Fig. 11-2. Diagram of a typical mitochondrion, as seen from electronmicrograph.

been placed. The homogenate can be spun in a centrifuge, and if this is done at various speeds, a fractionation or separation of the cell constituents will occur. When Warburg did this, he found that most of the enzymes responsible for the oxidation of the acids that we now know are intermediates in the Krebs cycle were contained in a large granule fraction, so-called because it could be spun down at low speeds. Like many observations, this one lay dormant in the collective biochemical mind for many years, though many biochemists did use the Warburg technique to determine some properties of these enzymes. But no one gave much thought to what was in the large granule fraction nor to what part of the cell contained all these enzymes. About 15 years ago, however, various biochemists became interested in just this problem, and led by such men as Claude, Schneider and Hogeboom, Lehninger, and Green, they repeated in essence Warburg's experiments, but with techniques made more refined by the accumulation of biochemical experience. Since they were also interested in cytology, they discovered the biochemical importance of mitochondria.

Cytologists had known about the existence of mitochondria for a long time. They had seen these microscopically small bodies in most cells of the body; they could stain them with certain vital dyes; and they knew that the mitochondria contained enzymes that could react with these dyes. After a dozen years of work with these mitochondria, biochemists now know quite a bit about them: they are the important constituents of Warburg's large granule fractions, all the enzymes of the Krebs cycle are found in these bodies, and they are therefore responsible for most of the energy transformation of the cell.

What is this mitochondrion? It is a structure, bounded by a limiting membrane, found in all cells except the bacteria and the mature red blood cells of the multicellular organism; it is found in plant cells, in algae, and in

---

Fig. 11-1. (*facing*). A: Mitochondria in rat liver cell (× 33,000). B: Mitochondria isolated from rat kidney (× 56,000). C: Mitochondria in an alga, *Chlamydomonas* (× 25,000). M, mitochondria; C, cristae; B, intramitochondrial bodies (function unknown). (Courtesy of G. Palade, Rockefeller Institute.)

protozoans. In all these cells its appearance is very similar: an outer membrane limits the structure, while just inside is another membrane that has folds or invaginations, called cristae, that reach deep inside the mitochondria, sometimes as far as the other side. This typical structure occurs again and again in cells, so that it is easy to recognize a mitochondrion simply by its morphology. Fig. 11-1 shows mitochondria from a rat liver, a rat kidney, and an alga, *Chlamydomonas*, as seen with the electron microscope. Fig. 11-2 is a diagram, derived from these electronmicrographs.

Enzymes in Mitochondria

Even when isolated, the mitochondria retain their typical appearance, although the process of isolating them has modified their texture, damaged their membranes, and made their outlines less sharp. These particles are nowadays separated essentially by the same method used by Warburg; that is, by first homogenizing the tissue in some medium, isotonic or hypertonic sucrose solutions being commonly used. By a process called differential centrifugation, the nuclei and unbroken cells are then spun down, and the supernatant from this spin is sedimented at a higher centrifugal force. The mitochondria come down in the form of a packed tan pellet. By washing this pellet several times, a fairly clean mitochondrial fraction can be obtained, and has been obtained from many kinds of animal and plant cells and even from some protozoans. Investigation has shown that the mitochondria from all these sources have almost the same enzymatic activities. In some cases, they seem to be the sole depositories of certain enzymes in the cell. Table 11-1 shows the results of a typical experiment in which a liver homogenate was separated into its various subcellular fractions by differential centrifugation. Of the total succinoxidase activity and cytochrome oxidase activity in the liver cell, some 60 percent in one case and some 80 percent in the other seem to reside in the mitochondria. The presence of these enzymes in the other cell fractions is thought to be due to contamination by whole or broken mitochondria. The fact that both these enzymes are concentrated in the mitochondria is shown by the observation that not only are most of their activities found there, but also that these activities are concentrated in this fraction; the amount of enzymatic activity per milligram of protein is greater in the mitochondria than in any other fraction and in the whole homogenate.

In some cases we can infer that all of a particular enzyme is in one compartment of the cell, for the enzymatic activities in other cell fractions— like the cytochrome oxidase activity in the small particle and nuclear fractions —are there as a result of contamination by mitochondria. Sometimes there is a cofactor for the enzymatic activity in some other cell fraction, as in the supernatant fraction; thus, although little or no enzymatic activity resides in the supernatant fraction, there is something there that when added to the

TABLE 11-1

Distribution of Succinoxidase and Cytochrome Oxidase Activities
in Mouse Liver

(Data from Hogeboom and Schneider)

Fraction	Succinoxidase		Cytochrome oxidase	
	activity	act./mg protein	activity	act./mg protein
Homogenate	4.25	1.34	6.86	2.06
Nuclei, cell debris	0.84	1.65	1.36	2.44
Mitochondria	2.40	3.18	5.39	6.46
Mito. supernatant	0.18	0.09		
Small particles			0.29	0.35
Final supernatant			0.00	0.00
Mito. plus super.	3.15			
Mito. plus nuclei, cell debris plus mito. supernatant	4.18			

mitochondria increases their succinoxidase activity. Experiments like these, in which recovery, activation, and recombination effects can be noted, have permitted us to determine the site of many enzymes and many cofactors in the cell. In just this way it was found that many of the enzymes of the Krebs cycle were localized in the mitochondria. This discovery, of course, could have been inferred from the early observation that mitochondria could oxidize pyruvate completely to carbon dioxide and water. Since we know that this can happen only via the Krebs cycle, we can say that all the enzymes of the cycle must reside in the mitochondria. In the case of some of these individual enzymes, there is also a large portion of the total cellular activity that is extramitochondrial. What these enzymes—for example, malic dehydrogenase—are doing outside the mitochondria, is not precisely known. Like all scientists, biochemists are willing to let awkward facts be laid aside for a while, until some theory has caught up with them. For the moment, we can say that the Krebs cycle is a mitochondrial cycle, and because it is an energy-transmutating cycle, we can call the mitochondria the energy transformers of the cell—the agents whereby the energy inherent in chemical compounds is modulated into the biological energy that is useful to the organism.

MITOCHONDRIA AS ENERGY CONVERTERS

The problem of biological energy is closely related to inorganic phosphate metabolism. As long ago as 1907, the biochemist Harden found that inorganic phosphate disappeared during cell-free fermentation in yeast. He further found that enzymes in yeast esterify this phosphate into organic forms, such as the hexose monophosphates and hexose diphosphates, which he later isolated from yeast cells. During the period 1930 to 1938, it was found that inorganic phosphate also disappears during the aerobic oxidation of carbohydrate, to be converted also into an ester form, which in this case was 1,3-diphosphoglyceric acid (see Fig. 14-2). We now know that these enzymatic steps are part of the glycolytic scheme, in which glycogen gets broken down anaerobically to lactate and during which some energy is made available. But respiration-dependent phosphorylation was not observed until Engelhardt in 1930 and Kalckar in 1937 did so.

It was in 1939 that the real start was made toward the determining of the role of phosphates in the oxidation of what we now call the Krebs cycle substrates. Many laboratories, rather simultaneously, observed that inorganic phosphate was necessary for the cellular oxidation of citrate, glutamate, fumarate, malate, and pyruvate; that without the addition of phosphate to the test tube, very little oxidation was observed. Hence phosphate disappearance and oxidation of substrate were coupled to each other. In muscle tissue the phosphate that disappeared was found to be esterified to creatine; and in kidney, liver, and muscle again, to be esterified to glucose, or fructose, or adenylic acid. The amount of phosphate that disappeared could be measured, and it was found that much more disappeared than could be accounted for by the then-known step of glycolytic phosphorylation—that is, the oxidation of glyceraldehyde-3-phosphate to 1,3-diphosphoglyceric acid (see Chapter 14). Hence it was proposed that the remainder of the phosphorylations occurred during the transfer of electrons from substrate to oxygen, the substrates being the familiar ones of the Krebs cycle. The object of research in those days was to find out how many moles of inorganic phosphate were taken up into organic form per atom of oxygen consumed during the oxidation of substrate. This ratio is a measure of the efficiency of energy production, of how much substrate has to be oxidized to give so much energy. This ratio would also provide some idea of the number of individual enzyme steps involved. Later on, as the Krebs cycle was fully worked out, it became very clear that most of the phosphorylations associated with the oxidation of substrate occurred not directly with the oxidation of substrate, but during the subsequent flow of electrons to the final electron or hydrogen acceptor, oxygen. For example, from Fig. 10-3 it can be seen that during the oxidation of α-ketoglutarate to succinate, one inorganic phosphate becomes esterified, to form guanosine triphosphate. But when α-ketoglutarate was oxidized completely by a tissue preparation, not one, but up to four moles of phosphate were esterified for every atom of oxygen consumed, or for every mole of α-ketoglutarate oxidized. Thus, three more phosphate esterifications had to be accounted for.

The Electron-Transport Chain

The electron-transport chain is the shorthand biochemical way of describing a reaction in which a donor transfers, with the aid of an enzyme, a pair of electrons to an acceptor. For example, pyruvate is oxidized by an enzyme that transfers a pair of electrons from pyruvate to an electron acceptor, this one being the coenzyme NAD, to form reduced NAD or $NADH_2$. The electrons are then transferred via a series of coupled oxidations and reductions to the final hydrogen or electron acceptor, oxygen, forming water. These electron transfer couplets have been known for a long time. The best known, cytochrome c, is an established pigment in biochemistry. But we now know that cytochrome c is only one of a series of respiratory pigments. Fig. 11-3 illustrates the current concept of the nature of electron transport from oxidizable substrate to reducible oxygen.

Many substrates are oxidized by enzymes known as dehydrogenases, so-called because they subtract two hydrogen ions and electrons from the substrate. Like most enzymes, dehydrogenases are specific for their particular substrate. In the Krebs cycle we speak of an α-ketoglutarate dehydrogenase, of a malate dehydrogenase, of a succinate dehydrogenase, and so on. In some cases, the dehydrogenase is a flavoprotein, for it consists of a protein plus a prosthetic group, in this case a flavin, and both together constitute the active enzyme. The hydrogen acceptor for some dehydrogenases is NAD, others use NADP specifically, and still others can use either NAD or NADP. NAD and NADP are known as coenzymes because they participate in the reaction directly by accepting electrons, thus becoming reduced.

The next step in the electron transport scheme is the oxidation of $NADH_2$ by an $NADH_2$ reductase; this enzyme is a flavoprotein in which the prosthetic group, flavine-adenine-dinucleotide, or FAD, becomes reduced and oxidized and thus participates in the reaction. There seem to be two flavoproteins at this point in the electron transport chain, one that couples, or works with the succinic dehydrogenase, and one that works in conjunction with the remainder of the dehydrogenases of the Krebs cycle. In the former case the electrons from succinate are transferred directly to the flavoprotein, while in the latter case the electrons go first to NAD, and then from $NADH_2$ to the FAD of the flavoprotein. These two reduced flavoproteins then give up their electrons to a common acceptor, cytochrome b, which then becomes reduced. In turn, cytochrome c_1, cytochome c, cytochrome a, and cytochrome a_3 become alternately reduced and oxidized by the passage of electrons. Somewhere along this chain is involved a newly discovered carrier, coenzyme Q_{10}, a quinone chemically related to vitamin K.

Finally, the enzyme cytochrome oxidase, which seems to be the entity that we now more succinctly call cytochrome a and cytochome a_3, catalyzes the transfer of electrons and hydrogen to oxygen to form water. All these cytochromes are heme proteins, in which the iron in the center of the heme becomes alternately oxidized and reduced. This shipment of electrons from the substrate to oxygen takes place because the energy potential of each of the intermediate carriers is such that the hydrogen or electrons go from a compound with a high reducing potential to one with a lower reducing potential. It is as if the electron transport chain were made up of a series of waterfalls: the water starts out at a high energy level, at substrate, and ends up at a lower energy level, at oxygen; this is naturally a one-way flow. However, the flow of electrons can be reversed under certain conditions by putting energy into the system, just as water can be made to go uphill if energy is applied (see below).

Oxidative Phosphorylation

It is logical to ask why the cell employs this complicated means of capturing the energy in substrate. The reason seems to be that chemically it is more efficient to break up the large difference in energy potential between substrate and oxygen into many small steps; and this is precisely what the electron transport chain does. At each waterfall, the energy latent in the chemical configuration of the substrate is not only captured but transformed into a chemical form that the cell can use. We now know almost precisely where these energy-transforming "waterfalls" are located in the electron transport chain; they are the places where ATP production takes place, and are so designated in Fig. 11-3. So we can say that electron transport phosphorylation is the coupling of the phosphorylation by inorganic phosphate of adenosine diphosphate (ADP) to give adensine triphosphate (ATP), with the concomitant transfer of electrons from a donor to an acceptor. We have some idea how this occurs (see below). We know more precisely that it takes place during the oxidation of $NADH_2$, during the oxidation of reduced cytochrome b, and probably during the oxidation of reduced cytochrome c. Thus for every substrate oxidized via NAD—that is, oxidized by an $NADH_2$-coupled dehydrogenase—there are three ATP molecules formed for every atom of oxygen that is reduced to form one molecule of water. In the case of succinate oxidation, the NAD step is bypassed and two ATP molecules are formed for every oxygen atom that is reduced. In some cases, as in α-ketoglutarate oxidation, during the oxidation of α-ketoglutarate by NAD there is also a phosphorylation step, a formation of GTP or ATP; this is an example of the so-called substrate phosphorylation, the production of energy

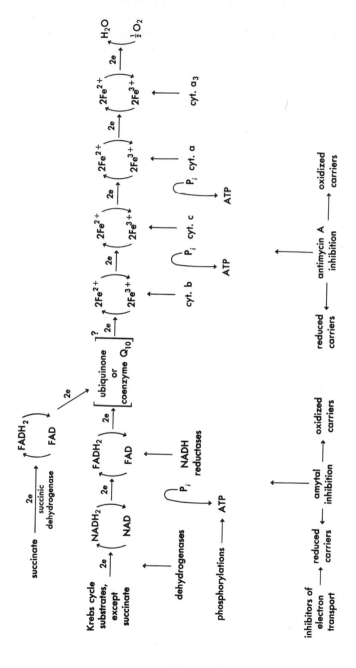

Fig. 11-3. Electron transport chain, showing sites of phosphorylation and sites of carrier inhibitions.

in the form of ATP by the direct oxidation of substrate. Another example of this is the oxidation of glyceraldehyde-3-phosphate to 1,3-diphosphoglyceric acid and the conversion of the latter to phosphoglyceric acid and ATP (Fig. 14-2). In the case of α-ketoglutarate, its oxidation will therefore give four molecules of ATP for each atom of oxygen reduced. This ratio, moles of inorganic phosphate esterified to form ATP per atom of oxygen consumed during the oxidation, is called the P/O ratio. It is a measure of the energy yield from the oxidation of a substrate; in the case of α-ketoglutarate it is four, with succinate it is two, with malate it is three, and with $NADH_2$ it is three. This over-all process, oxidative phosphorylation, is measured simply by adding substrate to mitochondria and observing the consumption of oxygen and the disappearance of inorganic phosphate. The P/O ratios that were observed during the oxidation of substrate showed that for each pair of electrons transferred to oxygen more than one phosphorylation step occurred. It is data such as these that produced the theory of electron transport phosphorylation.

Control of Respiration

The term coupled phosphorylation needs explanation. In the working mitochondria, no oxidation of many of the substrates of the Krebs cycle takes place without a concomitant phosphorylation. This can be shown very easily by studies with isolated mitochondria. It has been observed many times that mitochondria would not oxidize α-ketoglutarate or pyruvate in the absence of inorganic phosphate and ADP. In the presence of inorganic phosphate, but without ADP, there is no oxidation; as soon as ADP is added, the substrate is oxidized, inorganic phosphate disappears, and ATP is formed. This coupling of phosphorylation to oxidation is mandatory; that is, normally the electrons are not transported unless a synthesis of ATP also takes place. ADP is a necessary component in order for inorganic phosphate to be accepted, to form ATP; addition of only ATP has very little effect on the oxidation. However, if ATP is broken down to ADP, oxidation ensues, and the ADP is then rephosphorylated to ATP. This can easily be done by adding the enzyme hexokinase, which catalyzes the transfer of phosphate from ATP to glucose to form glucose-6-phosphate and ADP, the ADP necessary for oxidation to take place. Table 11-2 shows a typical experiment in which the addition of hexokinase, in the presence of ATP and glucose, causes an increase in the oxidation of pyruvate and fumarate. This effect of ADP is called the "phosphate acceptor" effect in increasing oxidation. Likewise, similar experiments have indicated the necessity of having inorganic phosphate present for oxidation to take place; the reason is precisely the same as in the case of ADP. Experiments such as these have firmly established the basis of the coupled oxidative phosphorylation of substrate in mitochondria. In the next chapter the possible meaning of this for the regulation of certain aspects of cellular metabolism will be discussed.

TABLE 11-2

Effect of Phosphate Acceptors on Oxidative Rate

Additions	Oxidative rate	
	pyruvate and fumarate as substrates	glutamate as substrate
ATP, inorganic phos.	12	8
Inorganic phos.	18	12
ADP, inorganic phos.	75	101
ATP, inorganic phos., hexokinase, glucose	80	116

KINETICS OF ELECTRON TRANSPORT AND ATP FORMATION

In recent years, brilliant work by Chance and his co-workers has verified the existence of the electron transport chain in mitochondria, in isolated whole cells, and just recently, even in various tissues of the animal *in situ*. In addition, this group has elucidated the kinetics of electron transport. Through the use of micromethods, of oxygen electrodes to measure oxygen consumption, and of rapid-flow double-beam spectrophotometry, and by simultaneous measurement of the reduced and oxidized states of the electron carriers, the sequence of electron carriers along the chain has been verified. Instead of measuring respiration by its end product, oxygen consumption, it has been measured by the reduction, not of oxygen, but of the intermediate electron carriers. Since each of the electron carriers has a characteristic absorption spectrum in the oxidized and reduced states, measurement of the concentration at the absorption peaks provides an estimate of the percentage of the compound that is reduced or oxidized.

Furthermore, as a result of these techniques we now know precisely where ATP is formed along the chain. Previously, separate parts of the chain could be assayed for their P/O ratios; the oxidation of one mole of reduced cytochrome *c* gave one mole of ATP, the formation of which must have occurred between cytochrome *c* and oxygen; the oxidation of succinate gave two ATP's, the other occurring between the succinate-linked flavoprotein and cytochrome *c*; the oxidation of NAD gave three ATP's, the third one occurring between NAD and cytochrome b. The very interesting result of Chance's work is that he came to exactly the same conclusion using radically different methods. Simply put, his method consisted of measuring the states of oxidation and reduction of the various components of the chain under conditions where (1) no substrate was added, (2) adequate substrate but no ADP was added, and (3) both adequate substrate and ADP were added. For example, if the mitochondria are starved of substrate, all the electron carriers become oxidized; during substrate oxidation and consequent phosphorylation they become reduced. If, however, substrate and a small amount of ADP are added to mitochondria, respiration rapidly increases until all the ADP is phosphorylated to ATP, at which time the respiration rate begins to fall precipitously. By observing the changes in the oxidation-reduction states of the various components during the latter inhibited stage of respiration, points along the chain—the so-called "crossover" points—can be identified as sites of energy conversion to a form that can be made available for the phosphorylation of ADP. Under these conditions, there occur reductions of NAD, flavoprotein, and cytochromes b and c, and an oxidation of cytochrome a. The "crossover" point is thus between cytochromes a and c, implicating this site as one of those where ATP formation could have taken place. These results were compared with those of experiments involving known electron transport inhibitors, as antimycin A and amytal. These react with the components of the chain as shown in Fig. 11-3 and cause a reduction of some components and an oxidation of others, thus identifying their points of inhibition. Thus, conclusions are now firmly drawn as to the sites of ATP formation, and even as to the possible mode of this formation.

Moreover we can now calculate by this method the amount of each of the carriers in the chain. They seem to exist in distinct stoichiometric relationships to each other; all the cytochromes and the flavoproteins are present in about equal concentrations, with about ten times as much of the pyridine nucleotides. From these values, and from the known figures for mitochondrial volume and protein content, one can calculate the number of respiratory assemblies for each mitochondrion; this amounts to a figure somewhere between 5000 and 10,000 sets of electron carrier chains.

Concepts of Coupled Phosphorylation

Another gratifying achievement of this method was to establish firmly the role of phosphate acceptors, like inorganic phosphate (P_i) and ADP, in the oxidation and reduction cycles of the carriers. The immediate changes in the reduction of these electron carriers that occur, within seconds, upon the addition of ADP strongly suggest a real chemical coupling between electron transport and phosphorylation. From the scheme given in Fig. 11-4, one can infer that not only is electron transport reversible, but the energy flow along

$$1. \; AH_2 + B + X \;\rightleftharpoons\; A + BH_2 \sim X$$

$$2. \; BH_2 \sim X + Y \;\rightleftharpoons\; X \sim Y + BH_2$$

$$3. \; X \sim Y + P_i^{**} \;\rightleftharpoons\; Y \sim P_i^{**} + X$$

$$4. \; Y \sim P^{**} + \overset{*}{A}DP \;\rightleftharpoons\; Y + \overset{*}{A}DP\text{-}P^{**} \; (ATP)$$

Fig. 11-4. Presently accepted hypothetical scheme for the coupling of electron transport to phosphorylation. A and B are electron carriers; X and Y are the hypothetical coupling compounds; P_i is inorganic phosphate; P_i^{**} is radioactive inorganic phosphate, and A^*DP is radioactive adenosine diphosphate.

the phosphorylation carriers can also be reversed. Recently, it has been found that when succinate and ATP are both added, the coenzyme NAD is reduced to $NADH_2$. This can be explained by the concept that upon the oxidation of succinate by its flavoprotein, the electrons flow first to cytochrome b; then, instead of electron flow to cytochrome c, the high energy of the added ATP causes a reversal, and the electrons go toward the NAD reductase, causing the reduction of NAD. ATP thus seems to be the energy source necessary to drive this reaction uphill, against the electrochemical potential. The tightness of the coupling between electron transport and phosphorylation is amply illustrated by the ease with which this reversible reaction takes place.

We do not know how this coupling occurs, but we have a fair idea of the individual enzymatic steps that must be involved. The scheme given in Fig. 11-4 is evolved from the works and thoughts of biochemists like Lipmann, Slater, Lardy, Lehninger, and Hunter, and is the presently accepted one. The central idea is that the coupling between electron transport and the associated phosphorylation occurs via an intermediate common to both these types of reactions. This need not be the case, but it is the simplest hypothesis to entertain at the present time, and it seems to fit the known observations. The experimental evidence that inorganic phosphate is not required for electron transport per se indicates that this common intermediate does not involve either P_i or ADP. Hence, it has been postulated that a reduced carrier (AH_2) reacts with the next carrier in line (B) in the presence of another substance (X), reducing B to BH_2. At the same time a high-energy bond (symbol, $\sim$) of about the same energy content as is in ATP is formed between BH_2 and X, giving $(BH_2 \sim X)$. The latter compound then reacts with another hypothetical substance (Y) to form the high-energy intermediate $(X \sim Y)$. At the following step, P_i finally comes in, forming $(Y \sim P_i)$, and once again, free X. $Y \sim P_i$ then couples with ADP, forming, finally, ATP, and free Y again. $X \sim Y$ is thus the intermediate common to both the electron carriers and the phosphorylation enzymes. Evidence for this scheme has been obtained in various ways. One could predict that reactions (3) and (4) should be reversible, involving as they do compounds of approximately equal energy content. One way to show this involves the use of the compound 2,4-

dinitrophenol; this compound has for some time been known to be an un-coupler of oxidative phosphorylation, for in the presence of small amounts of the compound, substrate, and ADP, oxidation proceeds at a fast rate but no phosphorylation ensues. This compound is also an activator of a mitochondrial adenine triphosphatase, splitting P_i from ATP. All these actions can be explained by postulating that dinitrophenol acts by causing $X{\sim}Y$ to be broken down to free X and free Y, and thus $X{\sim}Y$ cannot act as an acceptor for P_i to form ATP.

Two other partial reactions of the phosphorylation sequence have been described; both are inhibited by dinitrophenol, hence are involved in the coupling of electron transport to phosphorylation. One is the exchange reaction between P_i and the terminal phosphate of ATP, measured by mixing the mitochondria with radioactive P_i and nonradioactive ATP and measuring the radioactivity in the isolated ATP. Another is a similar exchange reaction between ADP and ATP, measured by incubating mitochondria with ADP labeled in the adenosine moiety and P_i, and then counting the labeled ATP. These are true exchange reactions in that there is no net synthesis of any of these compounds; no more ATP comes out than is put in. Reactions (3) plus (4) could explain the P_i-ATP exchange reaction, and reaction (4) could explain the ADP-ATP exchange. The identities of the hypothetical couplers, X and Y, are unknown. Both, or either, might be a phosphorylated enzyme. Recently, compounds such as an enzyme-bound "activated" NAD, or an enzyme-bound "activated" cytochrome c, or an enzyme-bound phosphory-lated histidine have all been implicated to function at some point in this scheme.

Also, certain quinones, like vitamin K or ubiquinone, another recently identified mitochondrial electron carrier, have been thought to be involved, perhaps as being compound X. Finally, we do not know whether these postulated Y's and X's are the same in all the three sites of phosphorylation along the chain, or if there are different couplers at every site. Since these partial phosphorylation reactions are tightly coupled to the electron transport chain, one might expect that the state of reduction of the electron carriers has some effect on the rates of these partial reactions; and indeed this is the case.

Submitochondrial Particles

The reason so much difficulty has been encountered in the solution of this problem of mechanism lies in the fact that the respiratory assemblies with their associated phosphorylations are a part of the insoluble lipoprotein membranes of the mitochondria. The laboratories of Lehninger and Green have made large strides in attempting to fragment these complex multi-enzyme units into workable pieces. These membrane fragments, which can be isolated by breaking up mitochondria with detergents such as digitonin or cholate, turn out to be miniature mitochondria, for it appears that the respiratory assemblies seem to be fairly evenly spread over the intact mitochondrial membranes. Perhaps they are the small granules, about 70 Ångstroms in diameter, that have recently been seen in specially prepared electronmicrographs and are shown figuratively in Fig. 11-2. A tentative idea that the cristae membranes, and not the outer membranes of the mitochondria, are the sites of these assemblies can be gleaned from the observation that heart mitochondria, which have more cristae per mitochondrion than liver mitochondria, also have a higher content of the respiratory pigments and a higher oxidative rate. These cristae are, like other membrane structures, lipoproteins (see Chapter 15); hence the respiratory assemblies are thought to be actually protein (enzyme)-lipid complexes. It is visualized that the lipid acts like a specific cementing substance, binding one particular carrier rigidly to its next neighbor. Thus electron transport is thought to occur not by molecular collision between the components of the chain, during which electrons are transferred, but by means of an actual flow of electrons, possibly through the protein matrix of the carrier, from one rigidly positioned carrier to the next. These miniature particles, lipoprotein in nature, have been called ETP, or electron transport particles. Adjacent to these particles, but still visualized as being part of the membranes, are most of the dehydrogenases of the Krebs cycle, and the protein enzymes that are involved in the phosphorylation reactions mentioned above.

Recently, attempts have been made to fractionate further this miniature multienzyme complex. Smaller particles have been obtained that contain some of the components and lack others. In this way, working with this jumble of particles and getting to know some of their properties, we hope to put together a meaningful chemical picture out of what is now simply a jigsaw puzzle. Some of these mitochondrial membrane fragments are themselves a complete assembly of the electron transport and phosphorylation chains. Similarly, the phosphorylation sequence system can be dismantled into fragments, as for example, those that contain only the dinitrophenol-activated adenine triphosphatase. One can now appreciate the structure of the mitochondrion; we can liken it to an efficient, structurally organized machine for the rapid transduction of oxidative to utilizable chemical energy.

Efficiency of Phosphorylation as an Energy Transducer

Let us now look back at what actually happens to the energy contained within a glucose molecule in the cell. If this glucose is completely burned in a test tube it will give about 690,000 calories of energy per mole, all of it as heat. In the cell, however, some of this energy is not lost as heat, but is retained in the form of ATP. The first reaction that glucose undergoes in the cell is the series of reactions called the Embden-Meyerhof scheme of anaerobic glycolysis (see Fig. 14-2). The first step in this process is the phosphorylation of glucose by ATP, by the enzyme hexokinase, to form glucose-6-phosphate. The latter compound is then enzymatically converted to fructose-6-phosphate, which then reacts with another mole of ATP to form hexose diphosphate, or fructose-1,6-diphosphate. This compound then goes through a series of reactions and eventually ends up as two molecules of 3-phosphoglyceraldehyde. This compound in turn is oxidized by NAD to give 3-phosphoglyceric acid and NADH. This reaction is actually a coupled phosphorylation step, for it occurs in the presence of ADP and inorganic phosphate, and ATP is thereby formed. All of the above enzymatic steps are performed by soluble enzymes, not found in mitochondria. Two moles of ATP are needed to start off the glycolysis of glucose, and during the oxidative reaction of glycolysis these two moles of ATP are regained.

The next steps all occur in the mitochondria. The $NADH_2$ that is formed as a result of the oxidation of 3-phosphoglyceraldehyde is oxidized via the electron transport chain to form three more ATP molecules. The end result of the glycolytic reactions is the production of pyruvic acid, in that two moles of pyruvic acid are formed from each mole of glucose. This pyruvic acid enters the mitochondria and is oxidized by NAD, giving over-all four moles of ATP. The 2-carbon compound that is formed, acetyl coenzyme A, condenses to form citrate, as explained in the previous chapter. The next energy-yielding step is the oxidation of isocitrate to oxalosuccinate, by NAD, forming $NADH_2$ whose oxidation then gives three more ATP molecules. The next step is the substrate-level phosphorylation of α-ketoglutarate to succinyl coenzyme A to give one more ATP, via GTP. The $NADH_2$ that is formed as a result of this oxidation is oxidized along the electron transport chain to give three ATP molecules. Adding up all these phosphorylations gives 19 moles of ATP formed from the oxidation of pyruvate to CO_2 and water; but since there are two pyruvate molecules formed from one mole of glucose, this one mole of glucose, on glycolysis and oxidation, gives 38 ATP molecules.

ATP is a so-called "high-energy" compound. By this we mean that if an ordinary phosphate ester link is broken, as that in glucose-6-phosphate, about 3000 calories of energy per mole are obtained, but if the ATP is hydrolyzed, the energy released is about 10,000 calories per mole of the terminal phosphate group in ATP. Multiplying all the ATP's formed from the metabolism of glucose gives $38 \times 10,000 = 380,000$ calories. This is about 55 percent of the total energy in glucose; in other words, the process is 55 percent efficient—a high rate. Probably about 90 percent of the energy liberated during the breakdown of foodstuff takes place during the process of electron transport. Thus we can see that most of the energy conversion—the conversion of that energy inherent in a chemical structure of the substrate to the energy inherent in the configuration of ATP—takes place in mitochondria.

Mitochondrial Membranes

The mitochondrial membranes are similar to others in being semipermeable; that is, some substrates, notably citrate, have difficulty in transversing the membranes, whereas ions like K^+ are seemingly taken up against a concentration gradient. Again, being bounded by such a structure, the mitochondria behave like osmometers, in that they take in water and swell when placed in hypotonic solutions. Under certain conditions of swelling they lose some of their low-molecular weight soluble components, like the adenine nucleotides and the coenzymes NAD and NADP, and hence lose their oxidative ability. Lehninger has found that certain kinds of swelling— that caused by the addition of phosphate ions, for example—are reversible; a very good reversing agent is ATP. Mitochondria swollen under these conditions will be contracted by the additions of ATP, extruding water. Indeed, on the basis of very fine measurements, it has been concluded that during the passage of electrons that goes on when substrate is oxidized and hence when phosphorylation takes place, there are distinct changes in the volume— presumably the shape—of the mitochondrion. It is intriguing that the mitochondria might contain a contractile protein that responds to ATP addition, for this is somewhat the same situation found in the contraction of muscle fibrils (see Chapter 14). What this alternate swelling and contraction of mitochondria has to do with the functioning of this organelle is not certain. But the main function of the mitochondria is not just the manufacture of ATP but its secretion to other parts of the cell. Thus it is believed that these changes in the permeability properties of the mitochondrial membrane, as indicated by the volume changes undergone by the mitochondria, have something to do with the need for the secretion of ATP. In addition to the phosphate acceptor effect noted above, any intra- or extramitochondrial influence on the permeability properties of the mitochondrial membrane could be a regulatory device for mitochondrial function.

The membrane is a decidedly functional structure. The mitochondria, and particularly their membranes, are a fine example of nature's conjoining of design and function to produce a structure that provides the greatest efficiency flow. No wonder mitochondria have been called the "powerhouse of the cell."

SUGGESTED READING LIST

Chance, B., and Williams, G. R., "Respiratory chain and oxidative phosphorylation," *Advances in Enzymology,* vol. 17 (1956), p. 65.

de Duve, C., and Berthet, J., "Use of differential centrifugation in the study of tissue enzymes," *International Review of Cytology,* Vol. 3 (1954), p. 225.

Ernster, L., and Lindberg, O., "Animal mitochondria," *Annual Review of Physiology,* Vol. 20 (1958), p. 13.

Green, D. E., "Electron transport and oxidative phosphorylation," *Advances in Enzymology,* Vol. 21 (1959), p. 73.

———, and Fleischer, Sidney, "Mitochondrial system of enzymes." In Greenberg, D. M. (ed.), 1960. *Metabolic pathways.* New York: Academic Press. Vol. 1, p. 41.

———, and Hatefi, Y., "Mitochondrion and biochemical machines," *Science,* Vol. 133 (1961), p. 13.

Hogeboom, G. H., and Schneider, W. C., "The cytoplasm." In Chargaff, E., and Davidson, J. N. (eds.), 1955. *Nucleic acids.* New York: Academic Press. Vol. 2, p. 199.

Howatson, A. F., and Ham, A. W., "Fine structure of cells," *Canadian Journal of Biochemistry and Physiology,* Vol. 35 (1957), p. 549.

Lehninger, Albert L., "How cells transform energy," *Scientific American,* September 1961.

———, "Energy transformation in the cell," *Scientific American,* May 1960.

———, Wadkins, C. L., Cooper, C., Devlin, T. M., and Gamble, J. M., "Oxidative phosphorylation," *Science,* Vol. 128 (1958), p. 450.

Novikoff, A. B., "Mitochondria (chrondriosomes)." In Brachet, J., and Mirsky, A. E. (eds.), 1961. *The cell.* New York: Academic Press, Vol. 2, p. 299.

Palade, G. E., "Electron microscopic study of mitochondrial structure," *Journal of Histology and Cytochemistry,* Vol. 1, (1953), p. 188.

Schneider, W. C., "Mitochondrial metabolism," *Advances in Enzymology,* Vol. 21 (1959), p. 1.

Siekevitz, Philip, "The powerhouse of the cell," *Scientific American,* July 1957.

Slater, E. C., "Constitution of respiratory chain in animal tissues," *Advances in Enzymology,* Vol. 20 (1959), p. 147.

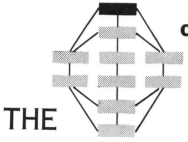

CHAPTER TWELVE

THE NUCLEUS AND THE STORAGE AND TRANSMISSION OF INFORMATION

So far we have talked about events that take place in the cytoplasm; we now turn our attention to the nucleus. All animal and plant cells contain well-defined nuclei, with a circumscribed membrane. Some cells have two nuclei and some have many. Bacteria, however, contain a "nuclear" region, unbounded by any membrane. Unlike the cytoplasm, which seems to have many functions, all the activities of the nucleus are geared to the timeless preservation and the exact reproduction of information. It is now well-established fact that the nucleus is the depository of the Mendelian factors, or genes, that these genes are located in chromosomes, that the primary chemical substance of the genes is deoxyribonucleic acid (DNA), and that it is this very large molecule, with a molecular weight numbering into millions, that carries the information that enables the cell to express its individuality. How this is done we do not know, but we are on the road to knowledge. This chapter will describe what might be called the initial travel along the highway.

There is a particular stain, Feulgen's stain, that reacts specifically with polymerized deoxyribonucleotides, that is, DNA. By means of this stain it has been shown countless times that DNA resides solely in the nucleus. Actually, the DNA is complexed with a basic protein, a histone, forming the naturally occurring nucleohistone. In a very few instances, however, in certain types of cells, there does seem to be also a small amount of DNA in the cytoplasm. The amount of DNA is constant; in all the cells of a tissue from an animal of a certain species, the amount of DNA per cell is the same. More precisely, the amount of DNA per nucleus is the same for all somatic cells of the particular animal, and this amount is twice that found in the germ cells of that particular species. We can go further and say that the amount of DNA per particular chromosome is a fixed amount and is characteristic of that species. This concentration of DNA remains the same no matter under what metabolic or nutritional strain the cells or the animal may be put. Another constant of the DNA of the nucleus is it metabolic stability. If radioactive inorganic phosphate is injected into an animal, the radioactive label will be found in high amounts in all sorts of phosphorus-containing compounds, but there will be no radioactivity in the phosphates of the DNA. It now appears that once the DNA of the chromosomes is synthesized, it does not break down. It is a stable molecule, and this is precisely what one would expect of a molecule that carries the information about the properties of the cell. This is not to say that the DNA is inert—in fact, we think it is not; it is to say rather, that once DNA is made, its molecular pattern is set and it does not undergo any further metabolic transformations. Being part of the chromosomes, the DNA does participate in cellular events (in fact, we can "see" it do so) when the chromosomes replicate and divide during cell division.

CELL DIVISION

This brings up the matter of cell division; why should a cell divide at all? We do not know for certain, but we can make good guesses. It may be that the growth of a cell, its increase in mass, has a certain upper limit, and that by dividing, a cell can obtain more surface area per mass of cell substance. In order to survive, the cell must have a constant interchange with its environment, be its environment the immediate minute one of a droplet of water or the intermediate one of the circulating blood. There probably is a limiting ratio of cell surface to cell mass, different for various kinds of cells, and when this limit is reached the cell divides. Another reason for division might be that there occurs a kind of "aging" of the cytoplasm; cell division would thus allow a cell nucleus, or nuclear material, to gather around it fresh cytoplasm and still not exceed the limiting ratio of volume to mass. Over-all, of course, the main reason for cell division during growth is to make new but similar cells, until the adult size of the organ is reached. What causes a cell of a young tissue to divide and what causes a cell of an adult tissue virtually to stop dividing are both enigmas.

Mitosis

We do know that the visible cause of cell division is nuclear substance replication. In the nucleus of a nondividing, "resting" cell—the so-called "interphase" nucleus (see Fig. 3-7)—all that appears is a dense, definite but unbounded area, which is the nucleolus; other less dense areas, not well-defined, lie in the nucleoplasm, that area of the nucleus outside of the nucleolus. However, though we cannot "see" structures in the nucleoplasm, we do know that some molecular organization is present. During cell division, mentioned in Chapter 3, this organization comes into prominence. Centrosome regions appear, one at each end of the dividing cell, which seem to act as focal points for the spindle fibers. The spindle fibers are part of an organization, the mitotic apparatus, that can be separated intact from dividing cells. In the nucleoplasm exist the proteins that later, during cell division, become condensed and so structured that they form the visible spindle fibers along which the chromosomes move to each end of the dividing cell (see Fig. 3-7). Clearly, there is much more work to be done in determining the molecular suprastructure of the nucleus and how this structure changes dramatically and rigidly during various stages of the nuclear cycle.

The division of a somatic cell into its two daughter cells is described by a process called mitosis (see Fig. 3-7). Essentially what happens in mitosis is that the exact distribution of the DNA is made in the nucleus, the DNA that had been exactly duplicated previously. Mitosis begins with the condensation of DNA, protein, and possibly RNA into visible chromatin threads, which now become the entwined, coiling chromosomes that can be seen for the first time. After division all that can be seen of the chromatin material in the interphase nucleus is a vague, dense area, which, however, does stain with Feulgen's stain, indicating the continued presence of the DNA containing threads. Thus we can say that if a cell is partitioned, it should be done in such a manner that the daughter cells have exactly the same characteristics as the mother cell. The significance of mitosis is that it provides a precise mechanism for this to be accomplished. In morphological terms, this means an exact duplication of the chromosomal number, size, and architecture, for the chromosomes carry the Mendelian genes. In biochemical terms, this must mean, as we shall see, an exact duplication of the chemical structure of the DNA.

DNA Duplication

The initial event in cell division thus seems to be the doubling of the DNA content of the nucleus. How this is initiated we have no idea, but it occurs sometime before the visible condensation of the chromatin material into the chromosomes. We are just beginning to find out how the DNA is

$$
\begin{array}{l}
n\ \text{dTPPP} \\
n\ \text{dGPPP} \\
n\ \text{dAPPP} \\
n\ \text{dCPPP}
\end{array} + \text{DNA} \xrightleftharpoons{\ \text{DNA polymerase}\ } [-\text{dTP}-\text{dGP}-\text{dAP}-\text{dCP}-]_n + 4(n)\text{PP}
$$

A

$$
\begin{array}{l}
n\ \text{UPPP} \\
n\ \text{GPPP} \\
n\ \text{APPP} \\
n\ \text{CPPP}
\end{array} + \text{DNA} \xrightleftharpoons{\ \text{RNA polymerase}\ } [-\text{UP}-\text{GP}-\text{AP}-\text{CP}-]_n + \text{DNA} + 4(n)\text{PP}
$$

B

Fig. 12-1. A: Equation for synthesis of DNA. (After Kornberg.)
B: Equation for synthesis of DNA-patterned RNA. (After Weiss and
Hurwitz.)

duplicated, for biochemists led by Kornberg have isolated from the cell
enzymes that will actually synthesize DNA (Fig. 12-1A). What the enzyme
needs for the reaction to occur are the four deoxyribonucleoside triphosphates
(deoxyadenosine, deoxycytidine, deoxyguanosine, and thymidine triphosphates), plus a small amount of DNA as a primer. During the reaction, inorganic pyrophosphate is split off from the triphosphates, concomitant with
the formation of the phosphodiester bonds between adjacent nucleotides. The
key substance seems to be the primer. The enzyme is specific for what kind
of bond is formed between the nucleotides and also is able to work only with
the deoxyribonucleosides; the ribonucleotides will not participate in the
reaction. However, the enzyme will not specify what kind of DNA will be
made; this is the function of the primer DNA. For example, we know that
if DNA is extracted from various sources and then hydrolyzed to its constituent deoxyribonucleotides, the amounts of these nucleotides, relative to each
other, are different for each "species" of DNA; these ratios seem to be a
characteristic of the DNA of that certain species. Thus, in the enzymatic
synthesis of DNA, the kind of DNA that is made depends on the kind of
DNA that is added as a primer; that is, the ratios of the various nucleotides
in the synthesized DNA are the same as those in the primer DNA. Furthermore, we think that a characteristic feature of each individual DNA
"species" is that its constituent nucleotides are linearly arranged in a certain
order along the DNA chain. And there is some reason to believe that the
DNA that is made during the enzymatic reaction has the same arrangement
of nucleotides along its length as does the primer DNA. In other words, it
appears that the primer DNA is really a sort of template upon which the
individual deoxyribonucleotides sit, and that all the enzyme does is to come
along and make the phosphodiester bond, zippering up the molecule.

The nature of the macromolecular structure of DNA makes all these
events extremely complicated. As discussed in Chapter 7, the native DNA
exists in a double-stranded structure, each strand being wound about the
other in a helical configuration. These helices are held together by hydrogen

bonds between the nucleotides, in such a way that the deoxyguanylic acid of one chain is hydrogen bonded to the deoxycytidylic acid of the other, and the deoxyadenylic acid of one to the thymidylic acid of the other. Therefore it would appear that in the enzymatic reaction in which the double-stranded DNA was added as primer, each strand was duplicated in such a way that where the primer DNA had deoxycytidylic acid, the synthesized DNA contained deoxyguanylic acid in the opposed position. Thus the synthesized DNA was double stranded also; each strand of DNA was copied in a mirror sort of way, resulting in two strands whose combined nucleotide composition and whose individual nucleotide arrangement was the same as the primer double-stranded DNA. It is thought that the DNA in the chromatin material of the nucleus is in this double-stranded configuration, and that DNA duplication in the nucleus takes place in much the same way as can be brought about in the test tube. However, DNA replication is not a requisite to cell division, for in certain cases the duplication takes place without cell division occurring. But the reverse is not true; cell division does not take place without a previous duplication of the DNA content.

Chromosome Duplication

The next general event in cell division is the prophase stage; this stage marks the convenient way of recognizing cells that are undergoing division. Here for the first time can be seen the condensation of the chromatin into coiling, spiraling threads, the chromosomes. It is generally agreed that the chromosome, that which is seen in the light microscope, is itself at least a duplex structure in the sense that it contains two, or perhaps more, equivalent strands, called chromatids. These chromatids are the structures that will be separated from each other at a later stage. Is one of these chromatids the new DNA that was synthesized upon the old DNA as template? It would appear that in some cases each of these chromatids is itself duplex, being made up of "half-chromatids," and that each of these half-chromatids are replicated, so that in time, a chromatid coil contains a new DNA strand and an old DNA strand.

The following experiment, first performed by Taylor (Fig. 12-2), permits us to observe what might be happening in the cell. The rapidly dividing cells were given radioactive, tritium-labeled thymidine, and then fixed for microscopic examination. In cells taking up the thymidine—those producing a new generation of chromosomes preparatory to division—all the chromosomes were found to be labeled, and radioactivity was equally distributed between the two chromatids of each chromosome. The cells were then placed in a medium of nonradioactive thymidine and a second generation of chromosome duplication was allowed to take place. Taylor found, by radioautography, that one chromosome was labeled and one was not. The simplest way

of explaining this, particularly in the light of present-day biochemical knowledge of DNA duplication, is illustrated by the diagram in Fig. 12-2. A chromosome consists of two parts or strands, each of which acts as a template for
the production of another part. In the radioactive medium, each of the chromosomes, after splitting in two, acts as a template for the production of a
radioactive partner. Therefore all the new chromosomes are labeled. However, when these labeled chromosomes duplicate in a nonradioactive medium,
the chromosomes will split to give a radioactive and a nonradioactive partner.
Each of these then acts as a template for new chromatid formation, yielding
chromosomes half of which are labeled and half are not.

This seems clear enough, but when we reach down into smaller dimensions we run into difficulty. We have no idea as yet of the molecular organ-

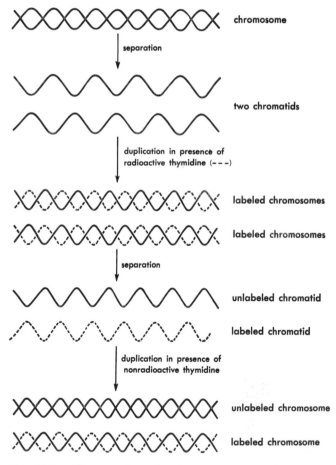

Fig. 12-2.   Diagram of results of radioautographic studies on
chromosome duplication. (After H. Taylor.)

ization of the chromatid, of how many strands of DNA it contains, of how this DNA is arranged within the chromatid. It appears that, somehow, the double-helix configuration of individual DNA molecules is reflected in the coiling of the thousands of times larger chromosomes. Thus, whereas at the biochemical level we can recognize that it is individual DNA molecules that are being duplicated, at the morphological level we are not sure what the corresponding duplicating structure might be—whether it is a whole chromosome, a chromatid, a half-chromatid, or an even finer subdivision of the visible complex.

This type of experiment can be done in another way, as shown by Meselson and Stahl, using cells of the bacteria *Escherichia coli*; the complications of chromosomal structure are avoided, for bacteria have no visible chromosomes. *E. coli* cells can be grown in a medium containing "heavy" nitrogen (N^{15}); thus all the DNA of the multiplying cells becomes labeled with N^{15}. If the growing culture is then switched to a normal N^{14}-medium, the DNA now produced will contain N^{14} in its bases. The DNA of all these cells can then be extracted, and by centrifuging it for a long period of time in a density gradient system containing cesium chloride, the N^{15}-DNA can be separated from the N^{14}-DNA. During the centrifugation the heavy cesium chloride molecules begin to be sedimented through the aqueous solution, setting up a density gradient. The heavier N^{15}-DNA molecules will be separated from the lighter N^{14}-DNA molecules in just such a system. If this separation is done at different times during the experiment outlined above, the following results obtain. At first, only one DNA band is visible, that of N^{15}-DNA. After one doubling of cell number, in the presence of N^{14}-thymidine, again only one band is found, but in a new position, intermediate between the positions that N^{15}-DNA and N^{14}-DNA would have occupied. After a second doubling, two bands of DNA are found, one in the same position as the previous intermediate band, and the other where N^{14}-DNA would have appeared. The intermediate band can then be isolated and separated in essentially the same manner into two bands, one made up of N^{15}-DNA and the other of N^{14}-DNA. The explanation of all these results seems obvious. The intermediate band came about because the N^{15}-DNA synthesized in the N^{15}-medium then served as a template for a newly synthesized N^{14}-DNA molecule. In the second division, both the N^{15}-DNA and the N^{14}-DNA chains served as templates for the synthesis of new DNA molecules. The N^{15}-DNA became linked to an N^{14}-DNA, to form another intermediate band, while the N^{14}-DNA served as a template for the laying down of another N^{14}-DNA, to form a new N^{14}-DNA band. Thus it would appear, in bacteria at least, and probably in all cells, that each DNA chain can serve as a template, or a primer, for the synthesis of another DNA chain.

On the biochemical level, we seem to have unearthed the mechanism of the exact duplication of an existing DNA molecule to form a new DNA molecule destined for the new daughter cell. On the morphological level, the mechanism is somewhat obscure, but the end result is the same: formation of a new chromosome that is the same as the one in the mother cell. It is thought that the inexactness of the duplication results in what can be observed grossly as a mutation; the new DNA chain is not exactly the same as the old one. But what exactly does this duplication of a structure within the nucleus portend with regard to the metabolism of the cytoplasm? We have said that both the nuclear and cytoplasmic characteristics of a cell are determined by the genetic material of the nucleus, the chromosomes. In other words, the synthesis of specific cellular protein, enzymes, and cellular structures is determined by the information in the genes. The question is, how are the instructions in the chromosomes transmitted to the recipient protein-synthesizing mechanism in the cytoplasm? The nucleus itself has, of course, some of the same reaction patterns as the cytoplasm. It can apparently make its own energy in the form of ATP, for it seems to have many of the glycolytic enzymes described in Chapter 14. It can synthesize various small molecules, and it has various enzymes to perform tasks whose relevance to the general metabolism of the cell is unclear. The nucleus has, then, its own complement of enzymes, in some cases the same types as found in the cytoplasm, in other cases different; but nevertheless these enzymes must be present in the nucleus of the daughter cell. The DNA of the chromosomes undoubtedly has the specification for the synthesis of these enzymes. But most of the enzymatic material, and much of the cellular synthetic machinery, is in the cytoplasm, and the information for the duplication of this material is also in the chromosomes.

ROLE OF RNA

The means by which transfer of information between DNA in the nucleus and the synthesizing machinery in the nucleus and cytoplasm occurs, is tied up with the metabolism of the other nucleic acid, ribonucleic acid (RNA). In the cells of mammalian tissues, about 10 percent of the RNA of the cell is in the nucleus. Of this, about 20 percent is in the dense nucleolar material (the nucleolus contains no DNA, though it does have some DNA material concentrated at its borders). The rest of the RNA is in the nucleoplasm, some of it being intimately connected with the chromatin material, and the rest possibly being in the form of small particles, ribosomes, which are also found in the cytoplasm (see Chapter 13). It has been known for some years that nuclear RNA, taken as a whole, has a high turnover. What this means can be illustrated by the following types of experiments. Radioactive inorganic phosphate can be injected into an animal, and the liver then removed and fractionated into its various morphological entities, such as nucleus, mitochondria, microsomes (see Chapter 13), and cell sap. The RNA is then extracted from all these fractions and tested for radioactivity. Invariably, the total nuclear RNA has been found to be the most radioactive when measured at intervals soon after the injection. In fact, in most instances it is the RNA in the nucleolus that is the most radioactive, as indicated by radioautographic experiments. In some cases, at later times after the injections, it has been found that the radioactivity of the total nuclear RNA has declined, while that of the total cytoplasmic RNA has increased. The same sort of experiment has been done with the technique of radioautography, using such favorable specimens as the large oöcyte cells; it is easy to determine in these cells whether the silver grains lie over the nucleus or the cytoplasmic areas. In these cases, it was again found that the nuclear RNA became radioactive more quickly than the cytoplasmic RNA.

The results of both these kinds of experiments led to the hypothesis that RNA is synthesized in the nucleus, and that these completed RNA molecules then move out into the cytoplasm. There is no doubt that something like this occurs, but there still remains the question as to whether all the RNA of the cell is synthesized in the nucleus, or whether there are two independent sites of cellular RNA synthesis, the other being in the cytoplasm. Certain experiments have raised the latter possibility. For example, using favorable types of cells where such a microoperation can be performed, it has been possible to remove the nucleus from the cell and still have a somewhat viable cell, at least for a short period of time. In most cases it has been found that there is no net increase in cytoplasmic RNA after the removal of the nucleus, while in a few cases there does seem to be cytoplasmic RNA synthesis going on, in the absence of the nucleus. However, we shall see in the next chapter that there are different kinds of RNA molecules, performing various functions, and the question of whether the nucleus synthesizes all the RNA of the cell will not be answered in full until finer techniques for working with separated RNA fraction have been developed. Even within the nucleus there seem to be different kinds of RNA molecules, as in the nucleolus and the nuclear ribosomes.

"Messenger" or "Informational" RNA

As will be discussed in Chapter 13, it is known that RNA is intimately connected with protein synthesis; this seems to be the sole role of the RNA molecules in the cell. Most of this synthesis of proteins takes place in the cytoplasm. From other lines of work, involving viruses containing RNA and not DNA, it is clear that the genetic material in these viruses is RNA. In these cases, the RNA of these particular viruses performs the same function as does the DNA in most other organisms and cells; that is, it contains the information for the synthesis of new viral protein. Thus, not only is RNA very similar in structure to DNA, but in some instances it can perform the same function. From these lines of evidence it has been postulated that the intermediate between the information in the DNA in the nucleus and the synthesis of protein in the cytoplasm is the RNA that is synthesized in the nucleus. There really has been no definite proof for this until recently. As first shown by Astrachan and Volkin, when bacteriophage, containing DNA as genetic material, infect bacteria, the infected cells synthesize a new kind of RNA molecule. This RNA seems to have the characteristics of the phage DNA in the sense that the base ratios of the newly synthesized RNA mirror the base ratios of the DNA. In other words, there seems to be information in the DNA for the synthesis of DNA-like RNA molecules.

It was also discovered, by Weiss and Hurwitz, that extracts can be made from bacteria, or from mammalian cell nuclei, that contain an enzyme that will make RNA. More to the point, the synthesis of this RNA was dependent on the presence of DNA (Fig. 12-1B). The enzymatic reaction utilizes the nucleoside triphosphates, ATP, CTP, GTP, and UTP; inorganic pyrophosphate is split off each of these, concomitant with the formation of the phosphodiester bond linking up the resultant nucleoside monophosphates to form the RNA chain. The enzyme is specific for the ribonucleoside triphosphates; the deoxyribonucleoside triphosphates are not suitable. Moreover, as in the case of DNA synthesis, the nature of the RNA product formed is dependent on the DNA that is added. It was found that the base ratios of the RNA synthesized (the relative proportions of the nucleotides to each other) were the same as the base ratios of the added DNA, as in the case of the phage-infected bacteria. When a different DNA, having different base ratios of its nucleotides, was added, the resultant synthesized RNA contained this base ratio. The enzyme was therefore making an RNA molecule that was the image of the DNA molecule. It can be envisaged that if double-stranded DNA is added, each strand will act as a template for the synthesis of an RNA molecule. Where there is deoxyguanylic acid in the DNA, there will be cytidylic acid in the RNA; where there is thymidylic acid in one, there will be adenylic acid in the other. In this way, the two RNA chains, taken together, will have the identical base composition as do the two DNA chains, taken together. This finding would neatly fit into a scheme that envisages the transfer of information from the DNA to the newly synthesized RNA, and thence from the RNA to the mechanism that synthesizes protein both in the nucleus and cytoplasm, but mostly in the latter. From histochemical and radioautographic evidence it is clear that DNA duplication and RNA synthesis in the nucleus take place at different times during the nuclear division cycle. At one time, the DNA acts as a template for the enzymatic synthesis of a duplicate DNA molecule; at another time, it acts as a template for the enzymatic synthesis of an RNA molecule similar to it. The means of the regulation of this twofold functioning of DNA is not known, but it is thought to be bound up with the macromolecular structure of the

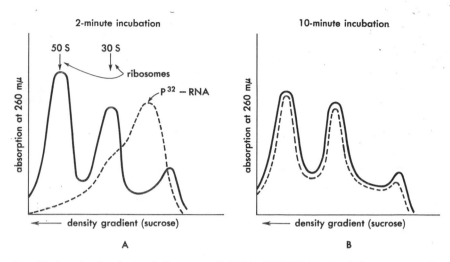

Fig. 12-3. A: Synthesis of "messenger" RNA (P³²-RNA). B: Subsequent attachment to ribosomes. (Data from McCarthy, Britton, and Roberts.)

DNA and possibly with the presence of the histone that is in combination with it.

Does the DNA-mediated RNA polymerase function in the cell as it does in the test tube? In the last two years many laboratories, notably those of Roberts, Spiegelman, and Gros, have been examining the *in vivo* behavior of the RNA that is probably synthesized by this enzyme in the cell. It has been called "messenger" or "informational" RNA, a name coined to denote the idea that it could fulfill the role of conveying a message from the nuclear DNA to the cytoplasmic protein-synthesizing ribosomes (see Chapter 13) as to the specificity of the proteins these ribosomes will manufacture. When a bacterial culture is given a single shot of an RNA precursor, labeled with P³² or C¹⁴, for a short period of time, one can easily notice the existence of an RNA fraction with a high turnover. The system favored for the separation of the macromolecules is a density gradient system, using either sucrose or the cesium chloride mentioned earlier. Ribosomal RNA, either in the form of intact ribosomes or extracted RNA, separates easily from nonribosomal RNA in such a system. Both types of RNA can be recognized by their characteristic absorption spectrum in the ultraviolet, with a peak at 260 mμ. Fig. 12-3 shows such a separation. The ribosomes under the particular conditions of this experiment have separated into two fractions, denoted by 30 S and 50 S particles (S = Svedberg units, a measure mostly of size). What is apparent is that the quickly labeled RNA, in this case with P³², does not appear to be ribosomal RNA. But after 10 minutes of incubating the cells in P³², most of the labeled RNA moves over into the ribosomal region. The interpretation first preferred, and still held by many workers in the field, was that the quickly labeled RNA was all "messenger" RNA; after it was synthesized it moved onto the ribosomes, and there, attached, acted as a specifying template for protein synthesis. Instead of the normal cell, phage-infected cell can be used, as did Astrachan and Volkin; the result is the same sort of picture as is illustrated in Fig. 12-3. Furthermore, as mentioned above, this newly synthesized RNA did seem to have the same base ratios as did phage DNA; it varied markedly in this regard from the bulk of the ribosomal RNA. In other words, this newly synthesized RNA fulfilled one of the requisites to qualify it as "messenger." However, the thought among many workers today—but perhaps not tomorrow—is that this newly synthesized RNA is partly of the "messenger" type and partly a precursor of ribosomal RNA; that the difference between these two types of RNA is not simply that one contains a code message from the DNA and that the other acts as a structural component of the ribosomes. What the relationship between the two is, we do not know; perhaps what we are witnessing is a counterpart, but on an unbelievably miniature scale, of some sort of punch-card indexing machine, with these two kinds of RNA macromolecules acting as the tapes.

However, at the same time investigators are firmly bound to the notion that such a "messenger" exists. One of the other properties of this postulated messenger—outside of its quick formation in the cell in certain circumstances, of its having the same base composition as the DNA, and of there existing enzymes that can make an RNA molecule based on a DNA template—is that this "messenger" RNA has arrangements of bases along its length that constitute a chain complementary to that of the DNA (see Fig. 7-8). If this is so, it would be expected that hydrogen bonds would be formed between these two complementary chains, in the same way as the two chains interact in DNA synthesis to form the tightly coupled double helix. That this occurs has been shown recently by Spiegelman and Hall. They used a technique devised by Doty and Marmur, that of making one polynucleotide chain become hydrogen bonded to another by heating a solution containing these macromolecules to about 40°C and then slowly cooling the solution. Doty and Marmur found that, during this cooling, the single strands of DNA began to attract each other, forming the double helix; this happens, however, only if there exist large stretches along these chains where the bases of one are complementary to the bases of the other—the prime requisite for formation of hydrogen bonds between them. This experiment can likewise be performed with a mixture of DNA and RNA macromolecules. If *E. coli* bacteria are infected with phage in a medium containing tritium-labeled thymidine, a precursor of DNA, phage DNA labeled with tritium (H^3) can be obtained. If P^{32} is also included in the medium, highly labeled "messenger" RNA can be obtained. The H^3-labeled DNA and the P^{32}-labeled RNA can be isolated and then separated from each other by means of a cesium chloride gradient, as shown in Fig. 12-4A. If, however, the solution containing the labeled DNA and RNA is given the Doty treatment, and the

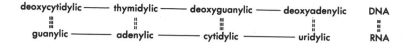

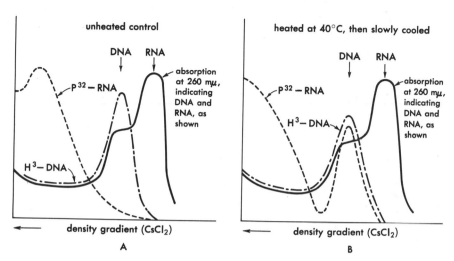

Fig. 12-4. Formation of complementary helices between DNA and "messenger" RNA (P³²-RNA). (Data from Hall and Spiegelman).

DNA and RNA are centrifuged in the gradient, there is a different result, that shown in Fig. 12-4B. Some of the newly labeled RNA, denoted by its P³² label, moves over into the H³-labeled DNA region. A complex has thus been formed, which behaves as a single sedimenting unit in the density gradient system. This complex formation is specific; if other DNA's—from other bacteria, from *E. coli* itself, from other phage—are treated under the same experimental conditions with the P³²-labeled RNA, the result is that shown in Fig. 12-4A, not that in Fig. 12-4B.

In the light of all that has been said about the structure of DNA and RNA, the only interpretation that can be made at present as to why a DNA-RNA hybrid is obtained in the above experiment is that along a large portion of the DNA and RNA chains there must be regions where the bases are arranged in such a sequence that the DNA bases are complementary to those of RNA. In other words, a real complementary copy of the RNA has been synthesized in the *E. coli* phage-infected cell, which mirrors a good deal of the DNA. Finally, Spiegelman's laboratory has shown, by similar techniques, that a complex of DNA and RNA can be extracted from the phage-infected cell, this complex containing the labeled RNA and hence the presumed "messenger" RNA.

In order to form the complex, the DNA has to be single stranded, for only denatured DNA (single stranded), and not native DNA (double stranded), will work. From other evidence we suspect that only single-stranded DNA acts as a template for "messenger" RNA. Thus it is clear that the double helix of the DNA must unwind before this RNA synthesis can occur. However, it is not clear whether one or both strands of DNA act in RNA synthesis. Some experimental results argue for the latter. Neither is it certain whether all the nucleotide sequences in the DNA act as a template for "messenger" RNA synthesis. It is thought now that all RNA synthesis in the cell is DNA mediated, be it informational RNA as above, or ribosomal RNA, or transfer RNA (see Chapter 13). We are therefore not certain that all the nucleotide sequences along the DNA chain are involved in acting as template for informational RNA synthesis. Again, where this "messenger" RNA synthesis takes place in the nucleus—whether in the nucleolus border, where there is chromatin material, or in the chromatin material of the rest of the nucleoplasm—is not known. How this RNA acts in the synthesis of proteins will be the subject of the next chapter.

In summary, the main biochemical function of the nucleus is twofold. It acts as a storehouse in the cell for the genetic information, which, upon cell division, is duplicated exactly for the daughter cells. It also acts as a storehouse for the information that, during the lifetime of the cell, informs the enzymatic mechanisms in the cytoplasm exactly which, and how many of, the protein enzymes the cell should synthesize. All the metabolism of the nucleus seems to be geared to these functions. Where they take place in the nucleus, we do not know. We are not sure of the biochemical "meaning" of the nucleolus, of the nucleolar-chromatin apparatus. All that we can surmise is that, in tune with the rigid exactness of DNA duplication and RNA synthesis, there must be a structural framework that is just as exact and upon which the biochemical mechanisms must rest.

SUGGESTED READING LIST

ALLFREY, V., "Isolation of subcellular components." In Brachet, J., and Mirsky, A. E. (eds.), 1960. *The cell.* New York: Academic Press. Vol. 1, p. 193.

BRIGGS, R., and KING, T. J., "Nucleocytoplasmic interactions in eggs and embryos." In Brachet, J., and Mirsky, A. E. (eds.), 1960. *The cell.* New York: Academic Press. Vol. 1, p. 537.

HOROWITZ, N. H., "The gene," *Scientific American*, October 1956.

HURWITZ, J., and FURTH, J. J., "Messenger RNA," *Scientific American*, February 1962.

KORNBERG, A., 1962. *Enzymatic synthesis of DNA*. New York: Wiley.

MCELROY, W. D., and GLASS, B. (eds.), 1957. *Chemical basis of heredity*. Baltimore: Johns Hopkins Press.

MAZIA, D., "How cells divide," *Scientific American*, September 1961.

———, "Mitosis and the physiology of cell division." In Brachet, J., and Mirsky, A. E. (eds.), 1961. *The cell*. New York: Academic Press. Vol. 3, p. 77.

MIRSKY, A. E., and OSAWA, S., "The interphase nucleus." In Mirsky, A. E., and Brachet, J. (eds.), 1961. *The cell*. New York: Academic Press. Vol. 2, p. 677.

PRESCOTT, D. M., "Nuclear function and nuclear-cytoplasmic interaction," *Annual Review of Physiology*, Vol. 22 (1960), p. 17.

STERN, H., "Function and reproduction of chromosomes," *Physiological Reviews*, Vol. 42, No. 2 (April 1962).

SWANN, M. M., "Control of cell division," *Cancer Research*, Vol. 17 (1957), p. 727.

TAYLOR, J. H., "The duplication of chromosomes," *Scientific American*, June 1958.

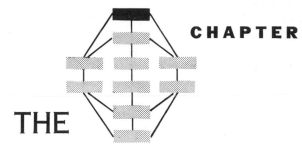

CHAPTER THIRTEEN

THE RIBOSOME AND THE UTILIZATION

OF INFORMATION

About fifteen years ago, biochemists began the use of radioactive amino acids in the study of the processes involved in protein synthesis. Up to this time there was thought to be very little protein synthesis and breakdown in the cells of the adult, nongrowing organism. It was assumed that once the cellular proteins were formed, they lasted the lifetime of the cell. There is, however, a constant excretion of ammonia and urea in the urine, and since these nitrogen-containing compounds could only have come from the catabolism of proteins, it was assumed that this steady excretion represented that small proportion of cells which were breaking down, their proteins being hydrolyzed, and the resultant amino acids deaminated to form urea and ammonia. This hypothesis of the relative metabolic stability of proteins was known as the "wear and tear" theory; that is, the only proteins being metabolized were those resulting from the breakup of dead and dying cells. It was thus a distinct surprise to find that, if one injected enough radioactive amino acids into an animal and then isolated proteins from the various tissues, these proteins were found to be radioactive. The radioactive amino acids had become incorporated into the protein molecules of the cell, proving that there is a synthesis of proteins in the cells of the adult organism.

This finding fitted in with the concept of the "dynamic state of body constituents," introduced by the biochemist Schoenheimer, to explain earlier findings on fat metabolism. According to this view, all the large compounds of the cell—not only proteins, but carbohydrates, fats, and nucleic acids—are constantly being broken down and resynthesized in the cells of a nongrowing organism. The present view is somewhat in between these two extremes; namely, that certainly there is some protein synthesis going on in all cells, but that most of it is due to the synthesis of protein for new cell formation and the synthesis of proteins for export from the cell. For example, when radioactive amino acids are injected into the animal and the proteins isolated from the various tissues, it is found that the tissues most active in protein synthesis are those tissues whose cells make protein for export purposes. Liver cells make most of the blood proteins; pancreas cells make most of the proteolytic enzymes destined for the gut; intestinal mucosal cells make digestive enzymes and some protein hormones; some endocrine glands make protein hormones for secretion into the blood. All these tissues are those that were found to contain the most radioactive proteins. On the other hand, tissues like skin and muscle were found to contain very little radioactivity in their proteins. In fact it was very clear that the second largest class of proteins in the body, the muscle proteins, exhibit very little breakdown and synthesis, or, as it has been called, protein turnover. There was some turnover, however, not for secretion nor for daughter cell protein, but simply a breakdown and resynthesis of a small part of the cell's own protein. What this represents is not certain at the present time.

Cytological Basis of Protein Synthesis

We can go further and delineate those cellular structures that are functioning in protein synthesis, in the following way. The liver homogenate can be fractionated by differential centrifugation into the morphological components of the liver cell. Thus the nuclear and whole cell fraction and the mitochondrial fraction are obtained. After the heavy nuclei and mitochondria have been spun out from the liver homogenate, the supernatant remaining from the mitochondrial centrifugation is spun at high speed; in this manner another pellet is obtained at the bottom of the tube. This pellet is called the "microsome," or small particle fraction. When this pellet is analyzed morphologically and chemically, it is found to contain most of the RNA and phospholipid of the cell and to be composed of fragments of the endoplasmic reticulum. Its importance to the economy of the cell was realized through the discovery that most of the protein synthesis of the cell took place in this fraction. After the liver is injected with radioactive amino acids, it is extirpated and fractionated into the nuclear and whole cell fraction, the mitochondrial fraction, the microsome fraction, and the supernatant fraction. The proteins from these different fractions are obtained and their radioactivity measured. Fig. 13-1 shows that the microsome fraction is the one with the

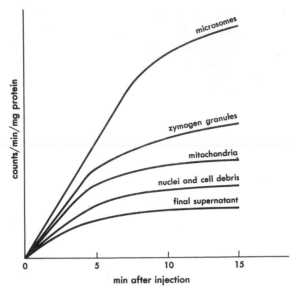

Fig. 13-1. *In vivo* incorporation of radioactive amino acids into proteins of various morphological fractions of pancreas tissue of guinea pig. (Data after Siekevitz and Palade.)

highest specific radioactivity, that is, radioactive counts per minute per milligram of protein.

But what is this endoplasmic reticulum? For years, cytologists had noticed in the cytoplasm of most cells a fine network or mesh, too diffuse and small to be made out clearly with the light microscope. When the electron microscope began to be used for biological specimens, it was quickly found that this network could be resolved into a number of membranes enclosing vesicular, or tubular, or flattened spaces in the cell, and that these spaces were probably interconnected with each other. In some cells, like secretory or glandular cells, there is an immense profusion of these membrane-limited spaces; in other cells, like muscle cells, they are diminished in number; in still others, like bacteria, they are nonexistent. Furthermore, in some cases the membranes are lined with tiny particles, whereas in other instances the membranes are bare. In general, we can describe the extramitochondrial part of the cytoplasm in terms of these structures, as follows: (1) cells with membranes free of particles; (2) cells with membranes all of which have particles on their surfaces; (3) cells with membranes with and without particles; (4) cells with no membranes at all, just particles; and (5) in a few cases, cells with a very few membranes and very few particles. In other words, the whole gamut of possible combinations is found.

Actually, "microsome" is a not very descriptive term, for it only describes what results from a method, that of spinning at high speed the supernatant from the mitochondrial fraction. Thus, if a cell has membranes with particles in its cytoplasm, then the microsome fraction is found to consist of the fragments of these membranes, still with particles on them. If the cell has only particles, then the microsome fractions consist of only particles; if only membranes, then the microsome fraction is a membranous fraction; and so on. For example, in pancreatic acinar cells, the cytoplasm consists of membrane-bound vesicles and spaces, most of these membranes having particles on their surfaces but some being bare, as shown in Fig. 13-2. The microsome fraction from pancreas is therefore composed of fragments of these membrane-bound vesicles, some with particles on their surfaces. This is shown in Fig. 13-2. In the liver, half these membranes have particles; thus the liver microsome fraction is markedly heterogeneous morphologically, being made up of membranes, of spaces between these membranes, and of particles on these membranes. It is also heterogeneous chemically, for most, if not all, of the phospholipid is found in the membranes whereas most of the RNA is found in the particles. It is heterogeneous biochemically, because the membranes have various functions (see Chapter 14), whereas the particles are intimately involved in protein synthesis. These particles, composed of RNA and protein, have been named "ribosomes"; their significance for our story is that they seem to be the intracellular structures that are involved in the synthesis of cellular proteins.

It seems strange that fifteen years ago no biochemist had a really good idea as to the function of RNA. The existence of these macromolecules had been known for a long time, and it was even known that RNA was present in both nucleus and cytoplasm but mostly in the latter. For many years it has been observed that certain cells, indeed only certain parts of these cells, are responsive to being stained with basophilic dyes; these cells are said to be basophilic because in them are concentrated large amounts of macromolecular acidic compounds that combine with basic dyes. We now know that it is the RNA in these cells that does the combining with these dyes. It was further observed that cells which were basophilic are exactly those which are known to be active in protein synthesis. This observation by Brachet was the first glimmer that RNA is involved in protein synthesis. Furthermore, it is the particles in the cell that are responsible for the basophilia, for it is the RNA of these ribosomes that combines with the basic dyes. Thus, those basophilic cells that are highly active in protein synthesis are just those cells that contain a large number of particles, some attached to membranes and some lying freely in the cytoplasm.

Protein Synthesis in Vitro

Next, it was found that this incorporation of radioactive amino acids into protein could take place in vitro, in the test tube. A homogenate can be made of an active tissue, like liver, and if the appropriate factors are incu-

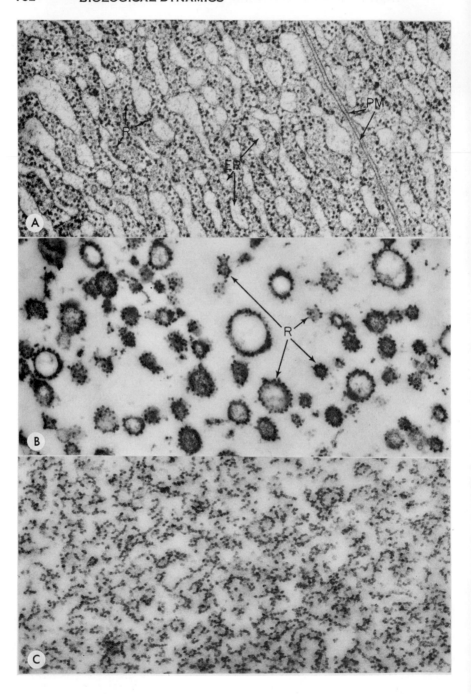

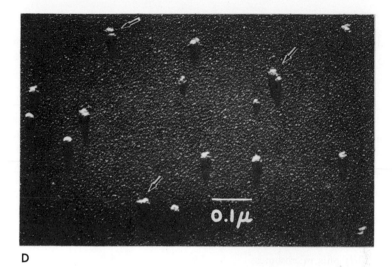

D

Fig. 13-2. (*facing and above*). The endoplasmic reticulum and microsomes. A: The endoplasmic reticulum in a pancreatic acinar cell (× 46,000). B: Isolated microsomes from a pancreatic acinar cell (× 39,000). C: Ribosomes isolated from pancreatic acinar cells (× 52,000). D: Isolated ribosomes from E. *coli*. 70 S particles indicated by arrows are made up of a 50 S and a 30 S particle (× 102,000). ER, profiles of the endoplasmic reticulum; R, ribosomes; PM, plasma membrane. (A, B, and C, courtesy of G. Palade, Rockefeller Institute. D, courtesy of C. E. Hall and H. S. Slayter, Massachusetts Institute of Technology.)

bated with this homogenate, the added radioactive amino acids are found to be incorporated into liver proteins. There actually is a net breakdown of protein during this incubation, but the presence of the radioactive amino acids makes it possible to detect that there is a small amount of protein synthesis; it is so small that only by the very sensitive radioactivity method could it be detected in the midst of the much larger breakdown. The most necessary additions were found to be oxidizable substrate and cofactors for the oxidation. In other words, the conditions that were found necessary for the incorporation of radioactive amino acids into protein were just those required for oxidative phosphorylation, for the synthesis of ATP (see Table 13-1). This finding was important because for years it had been thought that the mechanism for protein synthesis and protein degradation was one and the same, that protein synthesis was just the reversal of protein degradation. The main reason why this was thought to be the case has to do with the need for the cell to synthesize not just any protein, but to make specific proteins. We also know of the existence of many proteolytic enzymes that are very specific in hydrolyzing peptide bonds only between certain amino acids. These proteolytic enzymes, like all enzymes, could theoretically

TABLE 13-1

Ability of Various Isolated Morphological Liver Cell Fractions
to Oxidize Substrate, Form ATP, and Incorporate Radioactive
Amino Acids into Their Proteins
(Data from Siekevitz)

Fraction	Oxygen consumption	ATP formed	Counts/min/ mg protein
Homogenate	37.4	4.0	10.8
Mitochondria	8.2	4.2	1.3
Microsomes	0.4	0.0	1.1
Supernatant	0.8	0.0	0.4
Mitochondria plus microsomes	14.0	4.1	10.2
Mitochondria plus supernatant	9.7	4.1	1.5
Mitochondria plus microsomes plus supernatant	18.8	3.8	4.3
Mitochondria plus boiled microsomes	9.7	4.4	1.2

catalyze a reversible reaction; thus hypothetically they could not only degrade specific protein to amino acids, but could synthesize them from the amino acids. But we now know that protein synthesis is not the reversal of protein breakdown; that, whereas it does not take energy to hydrolyze a protein, it does take energy to build one up.

The homogenate that had been incubated with substrate, cofactors, and radioactive amino acid can, after various times of incubation, be fractionated into its different subcellular fractions. Again, the proteins of the microsome fraction are found to be the most radioactive of all the cell fractions (Fig. 13-3); since the picture in this *in vitro* experiment is the same as in the *in vivo* experiment (Fig. 13-1), it seems certain that experiments with the microsome fraction *in vitro* is somewhat a mirror of what happens inside the cell.

Going further, incorporation of radioactive amino acids into protein can be obtained if there are mitochondria oxidizing substrate in the presence of the necessary phosphorylation factors, and if there are microsomes, containing the ribosomes, plus some other factors in the supernatant. This is shown in Table 13-1, where it can be seen that both mitochondria, to supply the energy in the form of ATP, and microsomes, to supply the protein-synthesizing machinery, are necessary for the incorporation to take place;

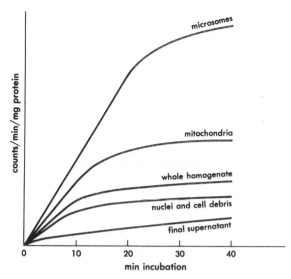

Fig. 13-3. *In vitro* incorporation of radioactive amino acids into proteins of various morphological fractions of rat liver homogenate. (Data after Siekevitz.)

either alone will not work. Later, modifications were made upon this basic system. Instead of mitochondria, ADP, phosphoenolpyruvate, and the appropriate purified kinase enzyme can be added to make ATP. Instead of whole microsomes, a pure preparation of ribosomal particles obtained from the fragmenting of microsomes, can be used. In some cases, as with bacteria or reticulocyte cells, a reasonably pure preparation of ribosomes can be obtained by homogenizing the cells and differentially centrifugating the suspension. Instead of obtaining amino acid radioactivity into a mixture of degraded proteins, we can isolate, as in the case of the reticulocyte cell, only one protein, hemoglobin, for these cells synthesize only this one oxygen-carrying heme protein. Thus, as can be seen in Table 13-2, from isolated ribosomes, an energy source like phosphoenolpyruvate and pyruvic kinase, amino acids, and various other cofactors, such as those contained in the "pH 5" fraction, we can make protein—in some cases, a specific protein.

Nature of Ribosomes

Because of the newly found importance of the ribosomes, much work has been done with them lately. These particles are ubiquitous elements found in all cells that synthesize protein, from bacteria to cells in the organs of mammals (see Fig. 13-2). As already mentioned, they are sometimes bound to membranous elements of the cell and in other cases lie freely in the cyto-

TABLE 13-2

Requirements of Isolated Ribosomes for the Incorporation of Radioactive Amino Acid into Protein

The complete system consists of liver ribosomes, ATP, GTP, $MgCl_2$, the "pH 5" fraction (which contains the activating enzyme, the transfer enzyme, probably other protein factors, and transfer RNA), and an ATP-generating system (phosphoenolpyruvate, ADP, and pyruvic kinase), and radioactive leucine. (Data from Kirsch, Siekevitz, and Palade.)

System	CPM/mg protein
Complete	66
Minus phosphoenolpyruvate and pyruvic kinase	7
Minus GTP	3
Minus ATP	3
Minus "pH 5" fraction	6

plasm. Their disposition in the cell seems to make no difference to their function; bacterial ribosomes, existing freely in the cell, make protein as well, or even better than, ribosomes from mammalian cells. Their size is always about the same: from 150 to 200 Ångstroms in diameter. Their constitution is also the same, for they contain from 40 to 60 percent RNA, the rest being protein. The RNA is of a very large molecular weight, estimated to be about 2,000,000 in various kinds of particles. What holds the RNA to the protein is not known, but it is believed to be either electrostatic forces, forming salt bonds between the phosphate groups of the RNA and the amino groups of the basic amino acids in the protein, or magnesium complexing between the same kind of groups, or perhaps a combination of both. The RNA can be removed from the protein by agents that break just such bonds, like strong salt solutions, or magnesium-complexing reagents. The ribosomal structure and appearance are strongly dependent on the presence and on the amount of magnesium. In the absence of magnesium in the medium, the larger particles fall apart to present a family of smaller particles, each of these smaller particles having the same RNA to protein ratio as do the original particles. Bacterial ribosomes probably exist in the cell as 100 S or 70 S particles (S = Svedberg unit), but they can be broken down to smaller 50 S and 30 S particles. Ribosomes from yeast and mammalian cells exist probably as 120 S and 80 S particles, and these can be split to 60 S and 40 S particles. It is not known how these smaller particles come together to make up the larger one, but Mg^{2+} complexing is thought to be involved. Which of these particles and subparticles are active in protein synthesis is not definitely known; research indicates that somehow the smaller ones fit together to form the larger ones, and it is the latter that are active in synthesizing proteins. There is also some indication that only a small proportion of the particles within the cell synthesize protein at any one time; what prevents the remainder from doing so is not known. The proteins of the ribosomes seem to be basic in nature, of somewhat the same kind that binds the DNA in mammalian cell nuclei. The nature of the RNA is unknown, but it is thought to act, together with "messenger" RNA, mentioned later, as a template for the synthesis of specific proteins. We do not know where it is synthesized, though the site is postulated to be in the nucleus (see Chapter 12); all that we do know is that the ribosomal RNA does not exhibit any turnover. In other words, it appears that once this RNA is made, it is stable and does not break down during the lifetime of the cell. Thus ribosomal RNA behaves like genetic DNA in being metabolically stable.

Mechanism of Protein Synthesis

What are the other factors necessary for protein synthesis to occur? To answer this we must go into some detail of what is known about the mechanism of protein synthesis. A few years ago Lipmann presented the idea that, in preparation for their role in protein synthesis, the different amino acids must be brought into a "high-energy" state. It was further hypothesized that this could be done only through the mediation of ATP. Looking for just such a reaction, M. Hoagland discovered the amino acid activating enzymes. ATP reacts with an individual amino acid, in the presence of this enzyme, to split off inorganic pyrophosphate and to form an amino acyl adenylate compound (Fig. 13-4). This compound remains tightly bound to the enzyme. There are specific enzymes catalyzing the reaction for each individual amino acid. The high-energy character of the amino acyl adenylate compound is indicated by the observation that when the enzyme is incubated with the amino acid, ATP, and the radioactive inorganic pyrophosphate, there is radioactivity in the ATP that can be isolated. Thus the reaction is easily reversible, showing that the energy content of the acyl bond in the amino acyl adenylate is approximately the same as that of the penultimate pyrophosphate bond in the ATP. The amino acid has become "activated."

The next step in protein synthesis was actually hypothesized by Crick before it was discovered. The reasoning was that if the ribosomes are involved in protein synthesis by containing informational or template RNA, there should be a carrier of the activated amino acid to the ribosomes, this carrier operating in such a way as to be able to "recognize" the RNA of the ribosomes. The RNA of the ribosomes was at that time postulated to have the information to make a specific protein—and what other molecule except another molecule of RNA was better suited for this role? The next step (Fig. 13-4) is the transfer of the amino acid, from its acyl binding, onto the adenylate moiety at the end of a certain type of RNA molecule, the so-called soluble, or transfer, RNA. This step is catalyzed by the same specific amino acid activating enzyme, and in the process, AMP is liberated from the amino acyl adenylate. There are specific RNA molecules for each of the amino acids, just as there are specific activating enzymes. Thus we can say that for each amino acid there is a specific activating enzyme and a specific transfer RNA molecule. Each of these transfer RNA molecules is much smaller than the RNA of the ribosomes, but it still is a relatively large molecule, being about 23,000 molecular weight and having from 70 to 80 nucleotides in its chain. The last three nucleotides (—cytidylic—cytidylic—adenylic) are the same in each of the specific amino acid transfer RNA's. In the transfer from amino acyl adenylate, the amino acid hooks up with the ribose moiety of the terminal adenylic acid, to form an ester bond. Again the reaction seems to be reversible, hence we are left to suppose that this ester bond is of a high-energy nature. This is the only known instance in which an ester bond is in equilibrium with a pyrophosphate bond of ATP; the reason why this is the case is not known at present. If, however, all the three terminal nucleotides of the different transfer RNA's are the same, then to account for the specificity of the RNA we must assume that in the rest of the RNA chain there are certain arrangements of the nucleotides that make for the amino acid specificity. And indeed, experiments that show exactly this point have recently been performed by Lipmann's laboratory.

The experiment bears a telling. First, the transfer RNA for alanine was isolated with radioactive alanine still attached to it; it can be designated as (alanyl—Tr.—RNA^{ala}). At the same time, the transfer RNA specific for cysteine was isolated still with radioactive cysteine attached to it (cysteinyl—Tr.—RNA^{cys}). The sulfhydryl group of the cysteine was then chemically removed, converting it to alanine, with no apparent effect on the structure of the transfer RNA. The result was an alanine residue attached to the specific transfer RNA for cysteine, that is, alanyl—Tr.—RNA^{cys}. This alanyl—Tr.—RNA^{cys} was then added to an *in vitro* amino acid incorporating system. As a cofactor was added a polynucleotide, a polyuridylicguanylic acid, which causes the incorporation of cysteine and several other amino acids, but not of alanine, into protein. It was found that, in the presence of this cofactor, the alanine of alanyl—Tr.—RNA^{cys} was incorporated into protein, but the alanine of alanyl—Tr.—RNA^{ala} was not. This result indicates very strongly that the amino acid specificity for incorporation into protein resides not in the amino acid attached to the RNA but in some specific portion of each individual transfer RNA molecule. The transfer RNA thus acts not only as a carrier, but as a specific "key and lock" carrier.

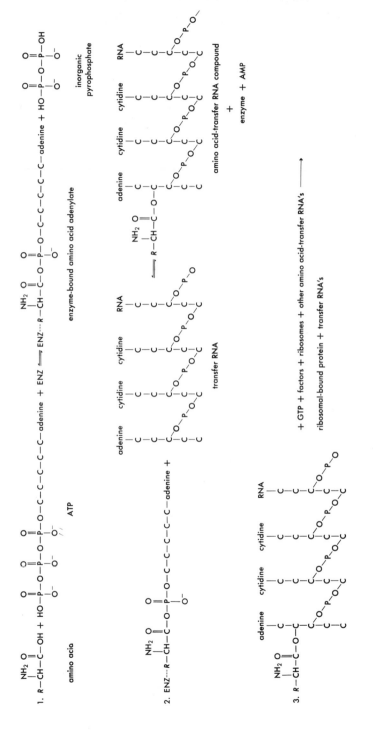

Fig. 13-4.   Enzymatic steps in protein synthesis.

The next step or steps in protein synthesis (Fig. 13-4) is by far the most baffling. We can set up *in vitro* test tube experiments in which the radioactive amino acid is linked to its specific transfer RNA; if ribosomes and certain factors are added, the result is radioactive protein bound to the surface of the ribosomes. We need, as cofactors, another high-energy compound, GTP, and two soluble proteins. One of the latter is probably the peptide-bond forming enzyme; what the other one is and what GTP does, is a mystery. In addition there seems to be a distinct step in getting the finished protein off the ribosomes and into the medium, or presumably into the soluble part of the cell matrix; again, the exact nature of this step is unknown.

From the work of Dintzis and Schweet, we know that in the reticulocyte ribosomes system that synthesizes hemoglobin—and probably in the syntheses of all proteins—the protein chain of the hemoglobin molecule is synthesized in a linear fashion, starting from the free amino-group end of the molecule; the reaction probably proceeds as follows:

$$
1. \quad NH_2{-}\underset{\underset{R^1}{|}}{C}H{-}\underset{\overset{\|}{O}}{C}{-}O{-}\text{transfer RNA}^1 + NH_2{-}\underset{\underset{R^2}{|}}{C}H{-}\underset{\overset{\|}{O}}{C}{-}\text{transfer RNA}^2 \rightarrow
$$

$$
NH_2{-}\underset{\underset{R^1}{|}}{C}H{-}\underset{\overset{\|}{O}}{C}{-}NH{-}\underset{\underset{R^2}{|}}{C}H{-}\underset{\overset{\|}{O}}{C}{-}\text{transfer RNA}^2 + \text{transfer RNA}^1
$$

$$
2. \quad NH_2{-}\underset{\underset{R^1}{|}}{C}H{-}\underset{\overset{\|}{O}}{C}{-}NH{-}\underset{\underset{R^2}{|}}{C}H{-}\underset{\overset{\|}{O}}{C}{-}\text{transfer RNA}^2 +
$$

$$
NH_2{-}\underset{\underset{R^3}{|}}{C}H{-}\underset{\overset{\|}{O}}{C}{-}\text{transfer RNA}^3 \rightarrow
$$

$$
NH_2{-}\underset{\underset{R^1}{|}}{C}H{-}\underset{\overset{\|}{O}}{C}{-}NH{-}\underset{\underset{R^2}{|}}{C}H{-}\underset{\overset{\|}{O}}{C}{-}NH{-}\underset{\underset{R^3}{|}}{C}H{-}\underset{\overset{\|}{O}}{C}{-}\text{transfer RNA}^3 +
$$

transfer RNA^2

3. n times

It is interesting that these results on the linearity of protein synthesis agree with the results of work on the genetic code. We would like to know more about this reaction, including questions as to the fate of the transfer RNA molecules, as to the forces holding the first amino acid onto the template, and as to why the amino group is the reactive group in peptide-bond formation, since the amino acid is "activated" at its carboxyl end. The latter aspect of the reaction mechanism is similar to that which occurs in fatty acid activation in the synthesis of long-chain fatty acids, for here too the carboxyl end is activated but the reaction occurs at the other, the methylene, end of the molecule.

Specific Protein Synthesis

The stability of ribosomal RNA, while comforting from a genetic point of view, pointed up a new paradox. If DNA is the genetic code in the nucleus, and the ribosomes are the protein-synthesizing machinery in the cytoplasm, then it must be the ribosomal RNA that has the genetic information, derived from DNA, that translates blueprint into concreteness. The finding of enzymes that synthesize RNA in the presence of DNA, and whose RNA has the same base ratios as does the DNA, serves to strengthen this argument (see Chapter 12). In bacteria the synthesis of certain new proteins—in this case, new enzymes—can be induced by the addition of substrate to the culture medium; the details of this induced enzyme synthesis are given in *Microbial Life*, in this series. The synthesis of new protein starts immediately upon addition of substrate, as can be measured very conveniently since the new protein is an enzyme, and this synthesis ceases very quickly after the bacterial cells are washed free of the substrate. Also, when bacteria are infected by bacterial viruses, or bacteriophages, the infected cells begin very quickly to make new enzymes necessary for the new syntheses of specific viral constituents. In the former case, the addition of substrate has somehow caused the cell to make new protein; in the latter case the DNA of the phage is the predetermining agent. However, in neither case does there seem to be any turnover of the bacterial ribosomal RNA; it is stable. Yet, if we have postulated that it is the ribosomal RNA that has the necessary information to make specific protein, how is it that when the cell is induced to make new protein there still is no perceptible change in the ribsosomal RNA?

Faced with this problem, several investigators, led by Jacob and Monod, have come up with the idea of a "messenger" RNA (see Chapter 12). According to the hypothesis, there exists an RNA molecule that is synthesized in the nucleus, or nuclear region in the case of bacteria, perhaps by just those enzymes using the triphosphates and DNA; this "messenger" goes to the cytoplasm, becomes bound to the ribosomes, and directs the ribosomes already in the cell to make specific protein. According to this view, the ribosomes are nonspecific protein-synthesizing machines. In the second case cited above, it is the DNA of the infecting phage particle that was conceived to be the directing force in the synthesis of the "messenger." It has been found that when a bacterial cell becomes infected with a DNA-containing phage, a very small percentage of the bacterial cell's own RNA undergoes a very rapid turnover, becomes synthesized, and is broken down very rapidly. Furthermore, if the base ratios of this rapid-turnover RNA are determined in a certain way, it turns out to have the same composition as does the DNA of the infecting virus. This type of RNA is probably a composite of RNA molecules of various sizes; and all of these molecules seemingly end up becoming bound to the pre-existing ribosomes of the bacteria. Therefore, as already mentioned in Chapter 12, there seems to be some experimental evidence for the existence of an RNA molecule, or a series of them, that does have the properties that have been proposed for "messenger" RNA.

However, as in all rapidly expanding subfields of science, there is also some evidence against this notion, or at least against the rather naïve idea propounded above. For example, the ribosomes from the reticulocyte cells— cells that are the precursors of red blood cells and that have no DNA—do have the capacity to synthesize hemoglobin; thus here it is not necessary for DNA to make messenger RNA that acts as a template for the synthesis of a specific protein. This discrepancy can be hypothetically overcome by the assertion that bacterial cells, doubling their number every 20 to 30 minutes and being very responsive to changes in the environment, are in need of an unstable messenger. Cells of the multicellular organism, on the other hand, have a much longer doubling time and have no need to be responsive to a changing environment, since their environment is a rather stable blood supply; thus they really have no need for an unstable messenger, and this "messenger" remains attached to the ribosomes as long as the cell lives. Some investigators, notably Roberts, have contended that what really happens when the bacteria are infected by virus is not the synthesis of new "messenger" molecules that later become bound to pre-existing ribosomes, but the synthesis of a very small number of new ribosomes, with the so-called messenger really being the RNA of these new ribosomes. Obviously, at present the picture is not too clear. Undoubtedly there is a fraction of cellular RNA that has a high turnover under certain conditions, and seemingly has the base ratios of the relevant DNA; a fraction like this has recently been uncovered in thymus cell nuclei and in the nuclei of regenerating liver cells. Its relationship to ribosomal RNA is unclear, however: some investigators look upon it as being, in part, a precursor for ribosomal RNA; others look upon ribosomal RNA, not as being a genetically coded carrier, but only as having a structural role in being able to bind the "messenger" RNA to it.

Furthermore, there is a dictum in biology, at present incapable of proof, that the DNA in all the somatic cells of the multicellular organism is the same. If this is so, and if the genetic information resides only in the base sequence of the DNA, then the genetic information is the same in all somatic cells. But we do know that the cells of one organ, of one tissue, are different from those of another; for one thing, they have different enzymes and thus different information is transmitted in each case to tell a cell that, for example, it is a liver cell and not a heart muscle cell. If the genetic information in the DNA is the same, there must be an intermediate in the chain between nuclear DNA and cytoplasmic synthesizing machinery that is not "messenger" RNA, that is not merely a replication of the DNA. This hypothetical intermediate could be either a differential subtraction or differential masking of the DNA from one cell to another. It has been postulated that the histone that is in a complex with the DNA in the nucleus acts as a masking agent in that only the "naked" DNA acts as a template for RNA synthesis. It is reasons like this which cast doubt on the hypothesis that there is a simple linear relationship between the genetic information in the DNA and the recipient of this information in the cytoplasmic ribosomes. It should be mentioned that the nucleus appears to have ribosomal-like particles in it also, and from the limited amount of work done with these particles it appears that these too are capable of synthesizing protein.

Nucleic Acid "Code"

We have been speaking of genetic information in the DNA, this information being precisely that necessary for the synthesis of specific proteins. We can say that in the DNA is a series of nucleotides that signifies that a certain amino acid be put in a certain place in a protein during the synthesis of that protein; in other words, the arrangements of nucleotides in the DNA might be a code for the arrangement of amino acids in a protein. Up until 1962, biologists in general had very little hope of even attempting to "break" this "code." However, physicists like Gamow, and physical chemists like Crick began to draw up mathematical postulates as to what kinds of theoretically possible codes would relate the four different nucleotides in the DNA, or in the RNA, to the 20 different amino acids in proteins. At present the most accepted code is that worked out by Crick and Brenner, in which a "word" of three "letters," or nucleotides, arranged in a certain sequence signifies a certain amino acid. There is some experimental and theoretical basis for just such a code. This code is believed to be nonoverlapping; that is, the code reads linearly along the DNA, or along the "messenger" RNA, and hence any one nucleotide along the nucleic acid chain can be part of only one "three-letter word."

It is now thought that this code can be broken, in the following way. It has been possible to isolate from bacteria enzymes that synthesize RNA from added nucleotide diphosphates. The enzyme is nonspecific in that it can synthesize any kind of polynucleotide molecule, the kind being dependent on the kind of nucleotides that are added to the incubation mixture. For example, if uridine diphosphates are added, the enzymes will make a polyuridylic acid; that is, uridylic acid molecules linked to each other by $3'-5'$-phosphodiester bonds. What the function of this enzyme is in the bacteria, and what the function of the RNA it makes is to the economy of the cell are not known. Nevertheless, the products of the enzymatic reactions have proved very useful, for now we can make many kinds of specific RNA-like molecules, of specified composition, practically at will, by merely varying the nucleotide diphosphates that are added as precursors to the incubation medium containing this useful enzyme. Thus, in addition to polyuridylic acid, other polynucleotides containing adenylic, guanylic, and cytidylic acids can be made, in various and known proportions of nucleotides.

One of these polymers, polyuridylic acid, was first used by Nirenberg in an *in vitro* radioactive amino acid incorporation system containing ribosomes from *E. coli* and the appropriate cofactors for amino acid incorporation to take place. When various radioactive amino acids were used, it was found that only in the case of phenylalanine was there a large increase in the incorporation of the amino acid into protein in the presence of polyuridylic acid. Thus, this polyuridylic acid acted like a "messenger" RNA. Similarly, when others of these synthetically made polyribonucleotides were added to the system, other amino acids were found to be specifically incorporated into protein. Here, for the first time, was a tool with which nucleotides could be experimentally related to amino acids. The results of using different polymers containing various proportions of the four different nucleotides, and using all the 20 amino acids as radioactive precursors in individual experiments can be set up in a table; from it can be ascertained that certain combinations of nucleotides seem to be the necessary ingredients for the incorporation of particular radioactive amino acids into the proteins of *E. coli* ribosomes. If three nucleotides in a row "mean," or signify, a certain amino acid, then we can say that three uridylic acids in a row "mean" phenylalanine. Table 13-3, which is a compilation of results from the laboratories of Ochoa and Nirenberg, shows that certain combination of nucleotides signify the various amino acids. The order of the individual nucleotides in each triplet is of significance, but not yet known. Some amino acids have more than one code word, as can be seen from the table, but what this portends is not certain. The present assumption, based also on other lines of evidence, is that the whole code may be degenerate; that is, a single amino acid may be specified by more than one set of nucleotides. This redundancy would reduce the chance of error in the translation of the code from nucleic acid to protein.

The order of the individual letters in the code words is not known, but investigators can make some guesses. Independent evidence has verified some of these code words for certain amino acids. For example, mutants of tobacco mosaic virus can be produced by chemical means, through deaminating with nitrous acid the RNA of the virus and thus changing the cytidine of the RNA into uridine, and the adenine to guanine. In the resultant protein coat of these mutant viruses it can be seen that some of the amino acids of the protein have been altered; some amino acids have been replaced by others in certain places along the protein chain, presumably as a result of the mutation caused by nitrous acid treatment of the RNA. Knowing what kind of changes in the RNA were produced by nitrous acid and knowing what amino acids

TABLE 13-3

Relationship of Nucleotide Combinations to Incorporation
of Amino Acids into Proteins
(Data from Nirenberg and Ochoa)

Nucleotides in postulated triplets	Incorporated amino acids
3 uridylic acids	phenylalanine
2 uridylic acids, 1 adenylic	isoleucine, leucine, tyrosine
2 uridylic acids, 1 cytidylic	leucine, serine
2 uridylic acids, 1 guanylic	valine, cysteine, leucine
1 uridylic, 2 adenylic	asparagine, lysine
1 uridylic, 2 cytidylic	proline
1 uridylic, 2 guanylic	tryptophan, glycine
1 uridylic, 1 adenylic, 1 cytidylic	threonine, histidine, asparagine
1 uridylic, 1 adenylic, 1 guanylic	methionine, glutamic acid, aspartic acid
1 uridylic, 1 cytidylic, 1 guanylic	glutamine, alanine, arginine

were replaced by others, we can make a correlation between these two events. Table 13-4 gives such a correlation. Compare Tables 13-3 and 13-4 and notice the marked similarity between the codes obtained by the two different methods.

Armed with this code, investigators can make predictions as to what nucleotides in a combination coded for a certain amino acid might be changed into another nucleotide coded for another amino acid. For example, different kinds of hemoglobin molecules can be isolated from humans with diseases characterized by specific changes in red blood cell hemoglobin proteins. It can be determined which amino acids in these proteins differ from their counterparts in normal hemoglobin molecules; thus, in some cases a glutamic acid in a certain position in normal hemoglobin has been changed to a glycine molecule in that same position. It was then predicted that these amino acid replacements could be due to changes in single nucleotides in the three-letter code word for certain amino acids, changing this into another code for another amino acid (see Table 13-5). In other words, the most common amino acid replacements could be predicted, simply on the basis of the probable frequency of changes of one nucleotide in a three-nucleotide code—changing, for example, uridylic-adenylic-guanylic acids to uridylic-cytidylic-guanylic acids. It appears that a code has been unveiled in which

TABLE 13-4

Examples of Agreement between Amino Acid Replacements in Tobacco Mosaic Virus Mutant Proteins and Experimentally Determined Nucleotide Code Words

The tobacco mosaic virus mutants were obtained by treating the virus with nitrous acid, which changes the RNA base cytosine to uracil, and the base adenine to guanine.

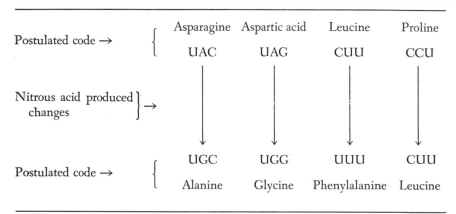

		Asparagine	Aspartic acid	Leucine	Proline
Postulated code →	{	UAC	UAG	CUU	CCU
Nitrous acid produced changes	→	↓	↓	↓	↓
Postulated code →	{	UGC	UGG	UUU	CUU
		Alanine	Glycine	Phenylalanine	Leucine

singular sequences in the DNA molecule can, probably through an intermediate RNA, code for the placement of specific amino acids into particular places in a protein.

Again, however, whether this is a real code, or a mirror of something much more complicated and mysterious, whether there is more than one code in which different nucleotide combinations code for the same amino acid—these questions remain. Workers in this particular field have reached the experimental point where they can take the ribosomes from E. coli, add the necessary cofactors for radioactive amino acid incorporation into proteins, add a certain kind of RNA, and obtain the synthesis of a specific protein. If tobacco mosaic virus RNA is added, it appears that tobacco mosaic virus protein is formed; if a certain phage RNA is added, a certain phage protein appears to be synthesized. It is not yet known what the E. coli ribosomes do; specifically, what the role of ribosomal RNA is in these syntheses. Possibly it simply acts as a structural feature of the ribosomes upon which the large protein molecules are to be built; or it may modify the RNA "messenger" in such a way that the ribosomes from liver, for example, make—in conjunction with the universal "messenger" from the universal DNA in all the cells of the organism—not universal protein, but specifically liver cell proteins.

TABLE 13-5

Examples of Agreement between Amino Acid Replacements
in Various Specific Hemoglobin Molecules from Various Sources
and Experimentally Determined Nucleotide Code Words

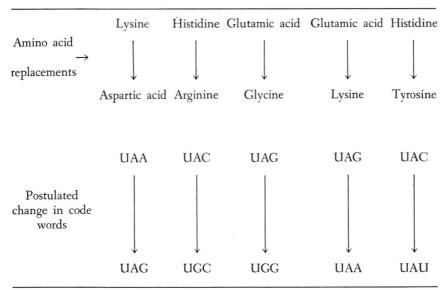

	Lysine	Histidine	Glutamic acid	Glutamic acid	Histidine
Amino acid → replacements	↓	↓	↓	↓	↓
	Aspartic acid	Arginine	Glycine	Lysine	Tyrosine
	UAA	UAC	UAG	UAG	UAC
Postulated change in code words	↓	↓	↓	↓	↓
	UAG	UGC	UGG	UAA	UAU

Synthesis of Structure-Specific Proteins

So far our discussion has centered on the amino acid sequence in proteins as determining protein structure; actually, a protein is a three-
dimensional structure with specific configurations. This configuration is very
important, because some of the properties of proteins as enzymes are due not
only to the amino acid sequence but also to the way the protein is folded,
folded to accommodate the substrate of the enzymatic action. It is presently
thought that once a protein has a specific amino acid sequence, it will
naturally fold into a particular configuration, and that this depends rather
more or less specifically on the distribution and conjunction of cysteine
residues in the protein, to provide disulfide bonds. It is these bonds, along
with hydrophobic bonds, that are believed to be the most important in keeping
the protein in a three-dimensional continuum. It is thought that once a
specific protein is synthesized, it will then naturally fold into its correct shape.
Moreover, not only must the cell synthesize a specific protein having particular
properties, but this protein has a predestined localization within the cell.
Cytochrome oxidase, for example, is a mitochondrial protein. How this enzyme
is finally placed in its correct position in the cell is completely unknown.

SUMMARY

To recapitulate, Fig. 13-5 shows our present ideas on specific protein synthesis, as detailed in this and the preceding chapter. One or both strands of DNA acts as a template for the synthesis of possibly all the RNA in the cell, probably in the nucleus. A part of this RNA is "messenger," a part is ribosomal, and probably a part is transfer RNA. There are indications that ribosomal RNA is synthesized in conjunction to the nucleolar-associated DNA. All these RNA species probably then move into the cytoplasm, a part possibly staying behind to act in nuclear protein synthesis. The informational RNA either forms part of the ribosomes or else it becomes attached to an already formed ribosome; investigators cannot at present distinguish between these two alternatives. Nor is it known whether ribosomal RNA picks up its protein in the nucleus or whether the completed ribosome forms in the cytoplasm. However, the ribosome, with its component or attached messenger RNA, has become a template for the synthesis of specific proteins. Meanwhile, the amino acids have become activated and subsequently have become bound to their own specific transfer RNA. The example given in the figure is phenylalanine; since the code word for phenylalanine is thought to be three uridylic acids (UUU), it is assumed that the transfer RNA has a region that "says" phenylalanine, and that this region is a three-adenylic acid (AAA) region complementary to the UUU region on the messenger RNA. The amino acid is thus now aligned in its correct position, according to the code for the specific protein that is contained in the messenger RNA. Thus set, the peptide bond-forming enzyme hooks up this amino acid with its adjacent amino acids. It appears that more than one enzyme is involved in this final step; what GTP does is likewise an enigma.

The final three-dimensional configuration of the synthesized protein is probably determined by the amino acid sequence; we can say that the primary structure of the protein, its amino acid sequence, is directly responsible for its secondary structure. At this time, some unknown release mechanism operates to peel the protein off its template. What happens to the messenger RNA and to the transfer RNA is not known for certain. In bacteria it appears that the lifetime of messenger RNA is very short, only lasting for the synthesis of a few proteins; in mammalian cells it appears to be much longer, possibly lasting the lifetime of the cell. We are equally unknowledgeable concerning transfer RNA, though here it does appear that the three end nucleotides (—CCA) have to be renewed each time this RNA acts as a carrier for the amino acid. Likewise, we do not know anything concerning the lifetime of the ribosomes, though it appears, from ribosomal RNA turnover data, that they last the lifetime of the cell.

Although it is clear that there are many hiatuses in this scheme, we believe that what we have here is at least a mirror to the truth. To complete

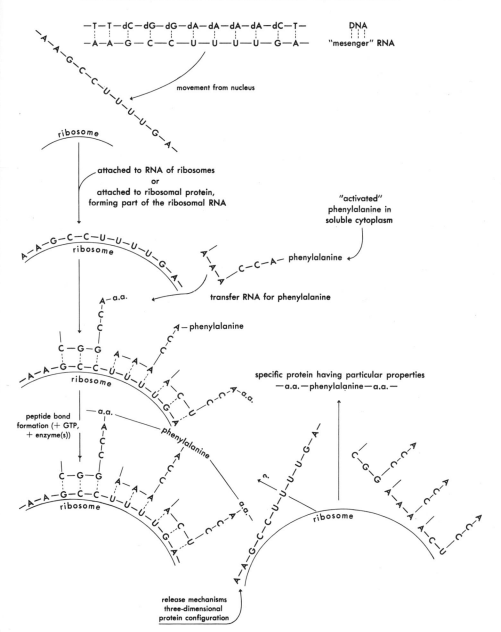

Fig. 13-5. Current idea of ribosomal protein synthesis (diagrammatic).

the picture, we have the tools of genetics to supplement our biochemical knowledge. Of course, even if we solve the mysteries of how the cell can unerringly continue to synthesize its very own specific proteins, we will still be left with the very important problem of how cell structure is formed (see Chapter 16). These problems include the formation of subcellular structures, the formation of cell structure that is distinctive for a given tissue or organ, and the factors determining the form and size of individual organs and even of the whole organism.

SUGGESTED READING LIST

ALLFREY, V. G., and MIRSKY, A. E., "How cells make molecules," *Scientific American*, September 1961.

BRACHET, J., 1960. *The biological role of ribonucleic acids.* New York: Elsevier.

CAMPBELL, P. N., "Synthesis of proteins by cytoplasmic components of animal cells," *Biological Reviews*, Vol. 35 (1960), p. 413.

CHANTRENNE, H., 1961. *Biosynthesis of proteins.* New York: Pergamon Press.

GROS, F., "Biosynthesis of proteins in intact bacterial cells." In Chargaff, E., and Davidson, J. N. (eds.), 1960. *Nucleic acids.* New York: Academic Press. Vol. 3, p. 409.

HOAGLAND, M. B., "Relationships of nucleic acid and protein synthesis as revealed by studies in cell-free systems." In Chargaff, E., and Davidson, J. N. (eds.), 1960. *Nucleic acids.* New York: Academic Press. Vol. 3, p. 349.

———, "Nucleic acids and proteins," *Scientific American*, December 1959.

HULTIN, T., "On the function of the endoplasmic reticulum," *Biochemical Pharmacology*, Vol. 5 (1961), p. 359.

INGRAM, V. M., "How do genes act?" *Scientific American*, January 1958.

McQUILLEN, K., "Ribosomes and synthesis of proteins," *Progress in Biophysics and Biochemistry*, Vol. 12 (1962), p. 69.

PALADE, G. E., "A small particulate component of the cytoplasm," *Journal of Biophysical and Biochemical Cytology*, Vol. 1 (1955), p. 59.

PORTER, K. R., "The ground substance: observations from electron microscopy." In Brachet, J., and Mirsky, A. E. (eds.), 1961. *The cell.* New York: Academic Press. Vol. 2, p. 621.

ROBERTS, R. R. (ed.), 1958. *Microsomal particles and protein synthesis.* New York: Pergamon Press.

SIEKEVITZ, PHILIP, "The cytological basis of protein synthesis," *Experimental Cell Research*, Supplement 7, (1959), p. 90.

ZAMECNIK, P. C., "The microsome," *Scientific American*, March 1958.

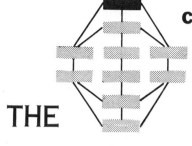

CHAPTER FOURTEEN

THE GROUND SUBSTANCE AND THE CONVERSION OF CHEMICAL ENERGY INTO WORK

The conversion of chemical energy to mechanical work is a universal property of all cells. In the multicellular animal organism, and perhaps also in the unicellular animals, the protozoans, a good deal of the energy produced in the form of ATP is consumed in the movement of the animal itself. In the former case, this means that ATP is utilized mostly for muscle movement. Excluding water, the substance in greatest amount in our bodies is muscle protein. About one-fifth the weight of the body is solid; 80 percent or more of this solid is protein; the greatest part of the protein in the body lies in the muscle cells. The importance of the production of ATP for muscle movement is thus apparent. There are three large problems concerning the physiology of the muscle cell: one is the recognition of the cellular components that actually perform the work; another is the continuous supply of energy that is needed; the third centers on how chemical energy is translated into mechanical energy.

MACROMOLECULAR COMPONENTS

The first task experimentally tackled was to find out what the mechanical elements are in the cell. Muscle cells are peculiar in that, apart from a nucleus and numerous mitochondria, they contain numerous elongated protein fibers that make up the bulk of the cell; these fibers seemed to be the key to the solution of this particular problem. The biochemist is never any happier than when he can tear something apart and see what makes these parts tick; if he is clever and lucky he can make a reconstruction, in the test tube and in his mind, as to how these separated parts fit into a biological whole. Fortunately, muscle tissue is amenable to being torn apart. Years ago, Szent-Györgyi, Bailey, Edsall, and Engelhardt began fractionating muscle cells, and biochemists have been following their lead ever since. Szent-Györgyi found at that time that a peculiar muscle protein, which he named myosin, could be extracted by strong salt solutions from muscle tissue; the myosin made up about 55 percent of the muscle cell proteins. The resulting viscous solution had a high double refraction of flow, indicating that the protein molecules in the solution existed as very elongated molecules. When ATP was added to this solution, the double refraction of flow practically disappeared, and furthermore, ATP itself became dephosphorylated. But the really exciting finding was that in the presence of a large amount of salt, myosin solutions could be squirted through a small orifice to form long threads, and these threads shortened when ATP was added. Later, it was found that another kind of extraction of muscle tissue produced the so-called glycerinated fibers, which could be made to contract more easily and more reproducibly when ATP was added. It had been known, mainly from the work of the physiologist Hill, that there is an energy requirement for muscle contraction, and that this energy requirement can be expressed in thermal or electrical equivalents. When it was also found that, during contraction, inorganic phosphate appeared and organic phosphate esters disappeared from muscle tissue, it became clear that ATP was ultimately the source of this energy.

As always, events became more complicated before they could be simplified into meanings. The extracted myosin was found to be actually made up of two kinds of proteins, myosin A, now simply called myosin, and another protein, actin; the two kinds were present in a ratio of 3:1. Myosin has a molecular weight of 400,000 and is about 1500 A long and 30 A in diameter; actin, of 70,000 molecular weight, is 300 A long and 30 to 50 A in diameter. This new myosin could split ATP but would not contract. When it was mixed with actin in the presence of potassium ions, however, a new complex was formed, called actomyosin; the actomyosin could not only break down ATP but would also contract in the process. The protein myosin, which when combined with actin seems to be the contracting fibril of muscle, is therefore also an enzyme, an adenosine triphosphatase, and has the properties of any other enzyme. More complications arose. There are two forms of actin, a G-actin (globular form) and an F-actin (fibrous form). G-actin can be polymerized into the longer fibrous form by the addition of ATP, and when this happens ATP is broken down to ADP and inorganic phosphate; thus G-actin can also act like an adenosine triphosphatase. The fibrous form, F-actin, is the one that reacts with myosin to form actomyosin; at this, a very large double refraction of flow appears, and when ATP is added, it is degraded and a contraction ensues. It thus appears that all the elements of physiological muscle contraction are known, but it has proven difficult to put them back into a meaningful biochemical picture. It is still not certain that what is observed in the test tube corresponds to the living muscle. For example, it is obvious that although an adenosine triphosphatase is somehow involved in muscle contraction, there must be a mechanism that relates to muscle relaxation, bringing the muscle back to the state of being responsive once again to the addition of ATP. Biochemists have been looking for this "relaxing factor," and have recently found a membrane fraction that will bind Ca^{2+} in the presence of ATP; it will inhibit adenosine triphosphatase activity but allow the ATP to react with actomyosin and thus keep the filament in a resting, relaxed state.

ENERGETICS

It is not certain that ATP breakdown is involved in the fundamental event of muscular contraction; in single-twitch type of experiments, no changes have been observed in the cellular ATP and ADP concentrations. However, in muscle cells there is another high-energy compound, creatine phosphate, or phosphocreatine. The compound is formed when the enzyme phosphocreatine kinase acts upon creatine and ATP, ADP also being formed in the process. This reaction is readily reversible—ATP being formed from phosphocreatine and ADP—thus indicating that the "high-energy" phosphate bonds in ATP and phosphocreatine are at the same energy level. Since there are large amounts of phosphocreatine in vertebrate muscle cells (a similar compound, phosphoarginine, exists in invertebrate muscle), it has been thought that it is a sort of energy storage compound in muscle. Moreover, some recent work indicates that it is indeed ATP that decreases in amount during a single twitch. But, no matter what the intimate mechanism may turn out to be, there is no doubt that in muscle cells there exist large amounts of high-energy phosphate compounds, ATP and phosphocreatine; that there is a decrease in high-energy phosphate during muscle contraction; and that, upon relaxation, a resynthesis of high-energy phosphate occurs.

The amount of muscular work depends on the initial concentrations of these compounds and on the rates of their re-forming. The efficiency of muscular work depends, as outlined in an earlier chapter, on the amount of free energy that can be obtained from a chemical reaction, the rest of the energy being lost as heat. In this case the over-all chemical reaction is the release of inorganic phosphate from ATP. Since we cannot do much to change the efficiency of this chemical reaction, let us think about the other possibilities governing the amount and rate of muscle movement: this has to do with how the muscle cell continuously generates energy.

Postulated Chemical Mechanism

First we should examine the diagram of Fig. 14-1. On the left is the situation in muscle cells as it may be visualized at present—though of course this concept may have to be revised in the light of new findings even as you read this sentence. Myosin reacts with ATP to form a myosin-ATP complex. In the presence of K^+ and F-actin, actomyosin-ATP is formed. This complex, when Ca^{2+} and Mg^{2+} are added, splits the ATP to inorganic phosphate, forming probably an actomyosin-ADP complex, which then breaks down to free actin, free myosin, and free ADP. Where in this scheme the contraction takes place is not exactly known, but it is believed to occur when the actomyosin-ATP complex acts like an adenosine triphosphatase. When the relaxing factor acts is even more of an enigma, though it is thought at present to act by binding Ca^{2+} and thus inhibiting the breakdown of the actomyosin-ATP complex. If this were all there is to it, only a single twitch would result, for unless the ADP can be rephosphorylated to ATP, the fibril will remain quiescent. This ADP molecule comes out of the muscle fibrils and can be acted upon in various ways. Two molecules of ADP can be attacked by the muscle enzyme myokinase, which catalyzes a transphosphorylation reaction, taking one phosphate from one ADP and placing it on the other ADP, to form AMP and ATP. In another pathway, ADP can react with phosphocreatine, by means of muscle phosphocreatine kinase, to form ATP and creatine. In both cases, ATP is being formed again, to be able to react with myosin. But these reactions are not the answer to the problem. In the myokinase reaction, there must be two ADP molecules to form one ATP molecule, whereas in the second case, there must be ATP to re-form phosphocreatine; this is why most biochemists look upon phosphocreatine as an energy storage compound, lasting for a short time, until ATP can be supplied in excess by some other means. This other means could be the glycolytic energy production.

In the early work with muscle fibers, it was found that if the fibers were electrically stimulated in the absence of oxygen, contraction nevertheless occurred but lactic acid accumulated. When the stimulation was continued for

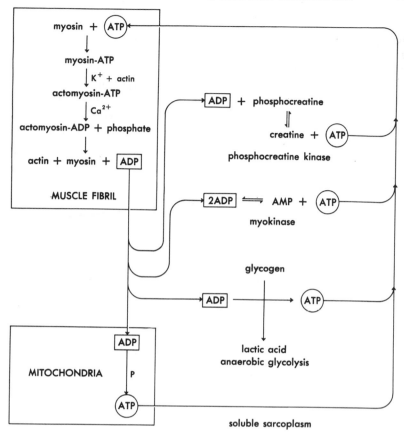

Fig. 14-1. Energy flow in muscle. (Redrawn from P. Siekevitz, *Ann. N.Y. Acad. Sci.,* 72, 1959.)

a while, the state known as "muscle fatigue" ensued. If this fatigued muscle were then exposed to oxygen, the lactic acid disappeared, and the muscle regained its ability to contract. If the muscle were to contract in the presence of air, no lactic acid would ever accumulate. When muscle was stimulated in the presence of iodoacetate—a poison that inhibits glycolysis, or the accumulation of lactic acid—it still contracted, but at the same time it was noticed that phosphocreatine broke down to creatine and inorganic phosphate. When this breakdown was complete, no further muscular contractions took place. Under all these conditions of anaerobic contractions and relaxations, the concentration of ATP remained unchanged. So you might say that under anaerobic conditions, at those times when the oxygen (blood) supply to the muscle cells is not adequate, muscle can contract by using up its store of phosphocreatine. This is what happens during sustained exercise; this store is replenished during exercise by the glycolysis of glucose.

Energy Supply: Glycolysis

Fig. 14-2 is a scheme of the glycolytic pathway in muscle, based on the work of C. Cori and G. Cori and of Meyerhof and Embden. Muscle glycogen breaks down to the 6-carbon sugar phosphate, fructose-1,6-diphosphate, via several intermediate enzymatic steps, including one that requires ATP. Fructose diphosphate is then split into two 3-carbon compounds, which are in equilibrium with each other. One of these, glyceraldehyde-3-phosphate, is oxidized to 3-phosphoglyceric acid, generating ATP. This step, catalyzed by the important enzyme glyceraldehyde-3-phosphate dehydrogenase, is the sole oxidative step in the whole glycolytic pathway. Oxygen is not required for this oxidation, only the presence of NAD, which is in the process reduced to $NADH_2$. Via several other enzymatic steps, pyruvic acid is formed, and at the same time another molecule of ATP is produced. Under anaerobic conditions, this pyruvic acid is reduced to lactic acid by the $NADH_2$ generated in the oxidative step of glycolysis, with NAD becoming re-formed, for further use in the oxidative step. Under aerobic conditions, pyruvic acid is oxidized via the Krebs cycle in the mitochondria, the formation of lactic acid being thus bypassed.

Since one ATP is needed to form fructose diphosphate, and since four ATP molecules are produced during glycolysis (two 3-carbon glyceraldehyde-3-phosphate molecules being generated from each 6-carbon sugar phosphate), a net production of three moles of ATP is obtained for each mole of glucose split off from glycogen. When lactic acid accumulates under anaerobic conditions, it travels to the liver via the blood, and there it is built into liver glycogen. Muscle glycogen is rebuilt by a process that starts with liver glycogen being degraded, and the liberated free glucose reaching the blood. From the blood it traverses the muscle cell membrane, is phosphorylated to glucose-6-phosphate, and is then transformed into glucose-1-phosphate. The glucose of this compound is then transferred into an "active" glucose compound, uridine diphosphate glucose, with the aid of UTP. This "active" glucose compound releases its glucose enzymatically to the end of the small amount of muscle glycogen molecules that are still present; in this way glycogen is built up of a very large number of glucose units. Since, by this pathway, one more ATP molecule is needed (by the enzyme hexokinase to form glucose-6-phosphate), the net result in glycolysis starting from free glucose is only two ATP molecules. Thus, either 20,000 or 30,000 calories of biologically usable energy in the form of ATP (about 10,000 calories per ATP) are obtained from a total heat energy yield of about 58,000 calories in going from glucose to lactic acid; this is an efficiency of from 30 to 50 percent.

The ATP that is thereby produced can phosphorylate creatine, thus re-

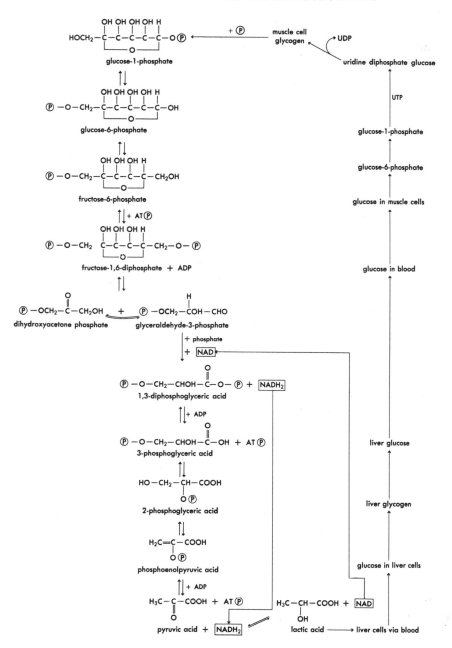

Fig. 14-2. Glycolysis in muscle cell.

building phosphocreatine again. This production of phosphocreatine will only last as long as there is muscle glycogen available. But, since muscle glycogen is being continuously re-formed from liver glycogen, we can say that liver glycogen is the ultimate energy storehouse for muscle movement. However, the whole anaerobic pathway, leading to lactic acid production, probably operates only under emergency conditions—either of sustained muscle movement, or of quick, large bursts of muscular exercise. Under aerobic conditions, lactic acid never accumulates, and the pyruvic acid is oxidized by the mitochondria; much more energy is thus gained from the essentially complete oxidation of glucose, via pyruvate, to carbon dioxide and water. When pyruvate is completely oxidized by mitochondria, 15 moles of ATP are obtained per mole of pyruvate oxidized, or 30 moles per mole of glucose. This is about 10 times the amount of ATP energy obtained from the anaerobic glycolysis of glucose.

Energy Supply: Muscle Mitochondria

For this reason it is not surprising to find many mitochondria in muscle cells, and more in heart muscle cells, whose fibers are continuously relaxing and contracting, than in the intermittently acting striated muscle cells. Fig. 14-3A shows a typical picture of heart muscle mitochondria among the fibrils, while Fig. 14-3B and C show the same situation as it exists in striated muscle. In both cases the mitochondria lie tightly apposed to the muscle fibrils, providing for a comparatively easy exchange of soluble materials between the two structures. In the former instance the mitochondria lie between the fibrils, while in the latter, the more numerous mitochondria lie close to the I bands. The ADP produced as a result of fibrillar contraction can leave the fibrils and enter the mitochondria; if there is enough oxidizable substrate available, it becomes oxidized, and concomitantly ADP is phosphorylated to ATP.

This entire system is probably a finely meshed one. Experiments on isolated mitochondria indicate that these mitochondria last longer, in a metabolic sense, when they are performing work than when they are not. If mitochondria are isolated and simply let stand at room temperature, they soon lose their ability to oxidize most substrates. If, however, they are made to oxidize substrate while they are left standing, they can continue to do so for a long period of time. Muscle tissue seems to be of the same nature: if the nerve connections to muscle are severed, making the muscle unable to function, in a relatively short time the muscle tissue starts to degenerate. We also know that muscle tissue can be made to "develop" by being made to work. What this means biochemically is that when muscle contracts and breaks down ATP to ADP, the ADP enters the mitochondria and there acts like a phosphate acceptor, as explained in an earlier chapter. If substrate is avail-

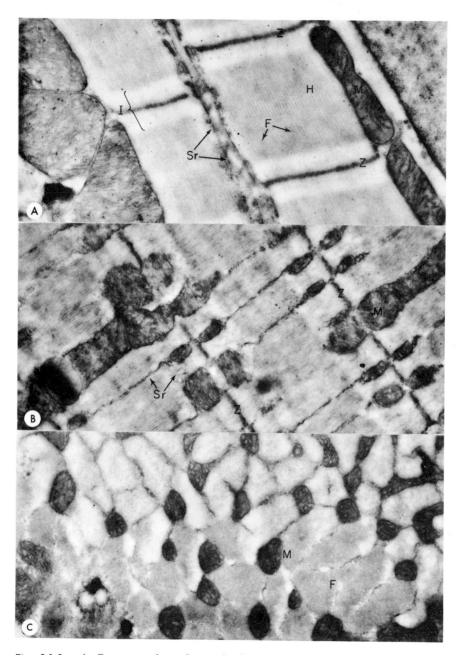

Fig. 14-3. A: Rat myocardium, longitudinal section ($\times$ 20,000). B: Striated muscle, longitudinal section ($\times$ 20,000). C: Striated muscle, oblique section ($\times$ 15,000). M, mitochondria; Sr, sarcoplasmic reticulum; F, myofilaments; Z, Z line; H, H zone; I, I band. (Courtesy of G. Palade, Rockefeller Institute.)

able, the release of ADP from the fibrils to the mitochondria acts like a stimulant to the mitochondria; substrate is oxidized and ATP is produced, and once again it can be recycled through the muscle fibril system. In other words, the mitochondria seem to be able to respond to ADP, to make ATP, as long as there is a need for ATP. If the muscle contracts continuously, a continuous supply of ADP will be fed into the mitochondria, which will respond by supplying ATP. If there is no need for contraction to continue, if there is no need for ATP, no ADP is formed, and hence no ATP will be generated. Because energy is precious, nature seems to have constructed a system in which no more biological energy is produced than can be used. It should be pointed out, however, that this idea of the symbiotic relationship between muscle fibrils and muscle mitochondria is based on the results of experiments with isolated mitochondria, and may have little to do with cellular reality. Nevertheless it does appear to many biochemists to be a really significant mirror of what happens *in situ* in the muscle cell.

GROSS MECHANICS

We know something about the energy requirement for muscle contraction and also a good deal concerning the molecular elements involved, but we still have much to discover about the gross mechanism. We know that the initial event is the depolarization of the muscle cell membrane that is affected by an electrical impulse from nerves. We also know a little concerning the gross structure of muscle and what happens to this structure during contraction. Muscle tissues are divided into three main classes: the smooth, the striated, and the heart muscles. Of the three, more is known about striated muscle. This is the so-called red musculature, the muscles with which we voluntarily move our bones, and it makes up by far the greatest amount of the muscle tissue. The other types of muscles are involuntary, that is, not under our conscious nervous control. Striated muscle bundles are so called because if one looks at them through a microscope, one sees clearly that dark bands transverse the fibers. These muscle bundles are composed of cells each having numbers of longitudinal fibers. These cells have many nuclei and numerous mitochondria, the latter lying between the fibers. The fibers terminate in tendons or directly to bones, hence contraction is brought about by a shortening of these fibers. The cellular fibers are in turn made up of individual fibrils, and it is the repeating striations of these fibrils that gives the name to this type of muscle. The repeating unit, of which there must be thousands in each fibril, is called a sarcomere. Fig. 14-3 shows a micrograph, while Fig. 14-4 gives a diagrammatic picture of a sarcomere, with the symbols universally connoting the different regions of the alternate light and dark, or isotropic (I) and anisotropic (A), bands. The Z lines serve as insertions

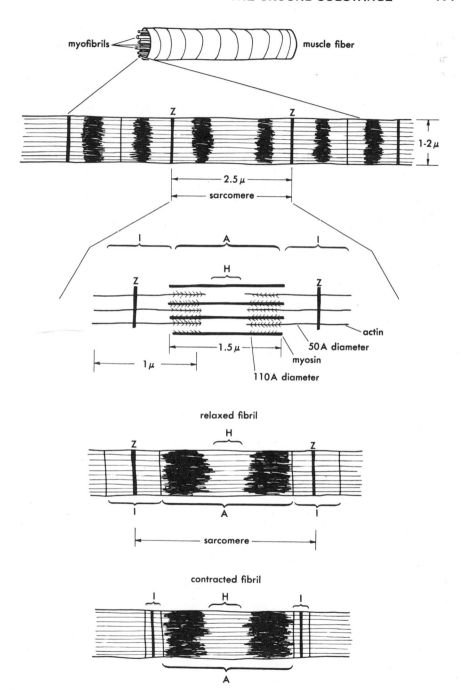

Fig. 14-4.   Structure of striated muscle (diagrammatic).

for a number (100 to 1500) of actin filaments, while the *A* region has in it from 50 to 750 myosin filaments. When muscle contracts, it seems that the light, less dense *I* zone practically disappears. There is no change in the length of the dark, dense *A* zone; indeed, it appears that this zone, particularly the *H*-zone segment, becomes actually wider. At present it is thought that fibrils composed exclusively of myosin make up a good part of the *A* zone, extending from the edge of one *I* zone to the boundary of the adjacent *I* zone. Actin seems to be found mainly in the filaments extending from the edge of the *H* zone, through the Z line, to the edge of the *H* zone of the adjacent sarcomere. Thus, it would appear that the actually contracting fibril, actomyosin, is found only in the *A* zone, on either side of the *H* zone. In fact, in some muscle fibers it has been observed by H. Huxley that there are actually cross bridges between the thin actin filament and the thicker myosin filament precisely in this *A*-zone region, outside of the *H* band.

Two mechanisms have been postulated to account for the contraction, but both agree on the existence of two kinds of muscle proteins, one being active or movable, and the other being anchored. In the one case, that of the folding mechanism, it is postulated that ATP breakdown causes certain long protein molecules to contract, somewhat like an accordion; the fixed-length muscle proteins that are attached to these contractile proteins are thus made to move along as the anchoring points move closer together. In the sliding-mechanism hypothesis, breakdown of ATP is thought to occur serially along the fibril; when this happens, the bonds holding the movable to the stationary proteins are consecutively broken, somehow allowing—perhaps because of opposite charges on the two proteins—one protein to slide over the other. In other words, it is proposed that actomyosin contracts by the movement of the actin filaments sliding over the myosin filaments when ATP is hydrolyzed; this would have the observed effect of bringing the Z lines closer together. At present the choice between these two hypotheses is toward the sliding mechanism, though really there is no conclusive evidence for either one.

Muscle cell physiology is an exciting and beautiful field. When we consider the intricacies of heart muscle, for example, in which principles of mechanics, chemistry, and electricity are finely combined into a whole that can function continuously for many years, we can only marvel. For the biochemist and cytologist, the muscle cell is that rare source which permits study of the efficient means by which nature transforms chemical energy into mechanical energy. In the not too distant future, we hope to know the precise mechanism.

SUGGESTED READING LIST

AXELROD, B., "Glycolysis." In Greenberg, D. M. (ed.), 1960. *Metabolic pathways*. New York: Academic Press. Vol. 1, p. 97.

FINEAN, J. B., 1962. *Chemical ultrastructure in living tissues*. Springfield, Ill.: Charles C Thomas.

HUXLEY, H. E., *"Muscle cells."* In Brachet, J., and Mirsky, A. E. (eds.), 1960. *The cell*. New York: Academic Press. Vol. 4, p. 365.

———, "The contraction of muscle," *Scientific American*, November 1958.

"Metabolic factors in cardiac contractility," *Annals of New York Academy of Science*, Vol. 72 (1959), Art. 12.

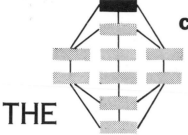

CHAPTER FIFTEEN

THE MEMBRANE SYSTEM AND THE EXCHANGE OF MATERIALS

All cells are constantly interchanging compounds with their environment. A single-cell organism, like a protozoan, bacterium, or yeast, takes from its surroundings its food and releases to it excretory, and in some cases, secretory, products. A cell of a multicellular organism must get its food from the circulating supply in the blood, and also secretes its waste products and sometimes its specific products, like blood proteins, sugars, or hormones, to the blood. All these exchanges are specific in that only certain compounds come in and only certain ones move out. The mechanism of this specificity resides almost wholly in the plasma membranes bounding the cells.

MEMBRANE STRUCTURE

Membranes can be isolated. The easiest method is to make red blood cell "ghosts"; all that is left after a certain kind of extraction is the plasma membrane. On the basis of chemical determination on these and other membrane fractions, it is now certain that the membranes are primarily lipoprotein structures, possibly with small amounts of other compounds bound to them. Lipoproteins are complexes between protein molecules and phospholipids or steroids, in which the ionized groups of the proteins, as charged amino groups, are electrostatically bound to charged groups of the lipids, the phosphate and hydroxyl groups. Fig. 15-1 is a scheme, similar to that originally proposed by Danielli, of the chemical appearance of a membrane, with protein covering the lipid layer. The 75-Ångstrom-wide unit has been named the "unit membrane," by D. Robertson, to denote its cellular universality. Its relationship to what is seen with the electron microscope is also indicated in the figure. The resulting structure has both hydrophilic and lipophilic properties, and is at once strong, resistant to shear and breakage, and yet flexible. But its greatest advantage as a membrane seems to be its property of semiexclusiveness, or semipermeability, which probably arises from the lipophilic nature of the structure, keeping out ionized molecules except under certain conditions. (The ionization of a compound markedly decreases its permeability across biological membranes.) It is these certain conditions that make for the specificity. Because of its hydrophobic nature, the membrane was long thought to contain pores; these would account for its permeability to small water-soluble compounds, for how else could even a small number of charged ions get through? There is, however, no evidence for the existence of pores, except for those so small as to allow water molecules to go through. It must therefore be assumed that other mechanisms for penetration exist.

Permeability Properties

The plasma membrane of a cell is not a static structure. It operates not only as a semipermeable barrier, but also as a vectorial one, in which the direction of flow of compounds is as important as the nature of the compounds. Because of this property, the membrane has the capacity to allow certain compounds to traverse the cell from a less concentrated solution outside to a more concentrated solution inside; that is, to move against a concentration gradient. For example, most cells keep their potassium ion concentration higher than that of the environment, and if this inside concentration should fall, the cell takes in potassium against the concentration gradient. Many other compounds behave in a similar manner, for all sorts of cells must have a mechanism to maintain a constant intracellular environment in the face of a variable external environment. From this fact alone we must assume that energy is required to transport materials across a membrane, for many of these materials are, so to speak, flowing uphill. In fact, it would appear that much of the energy of the cell is utilized in just this transport of materials in and out of the cell.

This is not to say that all materials are actively conveyed, against concentration gradients; some pass through the membranes by simple diffusion,

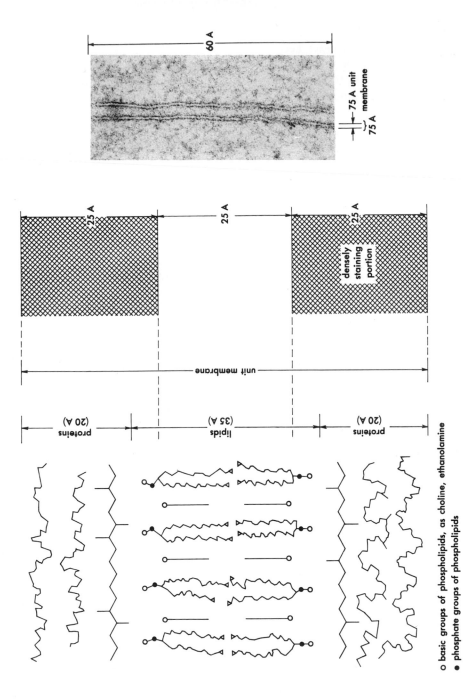

Fig. 15-1. Chemical diagram of unit membrane, and membrane as seen in electron microscope. (After Danielli, Robertson; micrograph courtesy of W. Stoeckenius, Rockefeller Institute.)

o basic groups of phospholipids, as choline, ethanolamine
• phosphate groups of phospholipids
△ end of fatty acid side chains of phospholipids
o— cholesterol

from a more concentrated solution to a less concentrated one. Nevertheless, a large number of membranes from all kinds of cells—from bacteria, to yeast, to red blood cells, to kidney cells, to epithelial cells, to muscle cells—are surprisingly impermeable to a large number of substances unless some process facilitates the passage of these compounds. Among these substances are many inorganic ions, both cations like sodium and potassium, anions like phosphate and sulfate, and sugars, amino acids, fatty acids, and even water itself. Again, it is surprising that these different kinds of cells behave quite similarly under the same experimental conditions; in other words, it appears that membranes of the biological realm have similar properties. Thus, experiments have been done with various convenient cells, such as the yeast cell, the red blood cell, or bacteria. The cells are incubated in a medium containing, with various additions, the compounds whose permeation is to be tested, and they are then spun down from this medium. The concentrations of these compounds, both in the medium and in the cells, are measured at the beginning and at the end of the experiment. In this way can be determined whether the cells take up the compounds, and also something about the mechanisms by which they do so. Sometimes preparations can be made of whole organs, like bladder or kidney slices, diaphragm or intestinal mucosal strips, or frog skin preparations, because in these instances the cells lining the organ or tissue are polarized; that is, they present one distinctive face to the outside and another to the inside, attached to the other cells of the organ. The structures on these two faces are quite different from each other; for example, many of these cells have on their outside the so-called brush borders, which are really fine villi, thus increasing the membranous surface area manyfold. In many cases even the interior of the cell is polarized, in that the mitochondria are at one end of the cell. But whatever the test cell, it appears that the same compounds are always kept out of cells unless there is a particular mechanism to get them in. From what we know so far, the same mechanism for the conveyance of potassium operates in all kinds of cells, the same mechanism for the movement of sugars operates in all kinds of cells, and so forth. Most of these mechanisms require an energetic coupling to transport, and this energy supply derives ultimately, and seemingly in some cases specifically, from ATP. Such an energetic coupling system has been given the name "active transport."

In the interior of most cells, the concentration of total potassium is much higher than it is in the immediate environment, and yet the element is mostly in the form of free ions, K^+. Magnesium appears to behave in a similar manner. The high concentration occurs, not because the membrane is impermeable to K^+, but because the cell can take in K^+ at a higher rate than it can leak out; thus there seems to be a vectorial coefficient to membrane permeability (Fig. 15-2). The maintenance of this intracellular concentration requires energy, for red blood cells and nerve cells—but not muscle

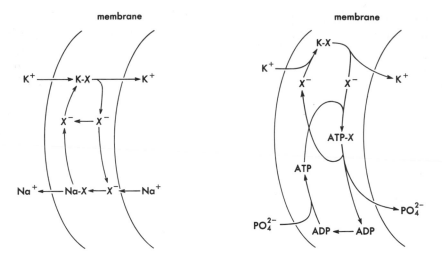

Fig. 15-2.   Postulated scheme for Na⁺ and K⁺ transport across membranes.

cells—will lose appreciable amounts of K^+ to the medium if kept under anaerobic conditions, and this loss can be prevented by the addition of glucose to the medium. The glucose is metabolized by the cells, thus indicating that the gradient for K^+ is maintained by a constant supply of metabolic energy. Actually, it is thought that the energy is involved in pumping Na^+ to the outside, with K^+ acting passively to maintain the ionic concentration. Somewhat the same mechanisms have been shown to hold for bacterial and yeast cells. In addition, in nerve cells, the flow of Na^+ and K^+ in and out of the cell is somehow connected with a polarization of the membrane; current flow along the nerve cell membrane seems to be correlated with a movement of K^+ from inside to outside the cell, with the Na^+ doing the reverse. The recovery phase—the depolarization of the membrane, readying it for the next wave of electrical potential—would then correspond to a movement of Na^+ to the outside and K^+ to the inside. Since in both cases the flow of the cation is against a concentration gradient, work has to be done and energy is required. Thus, in the case of the nerve cell, two mechanisms of ion transport are operating, one connected with an electrochemical gradient and dependent on an outside stimulus, and the other dependent on an energy supply generated by the cell itself.

The membrane around the muscle fibers, called the sarcolemma, is also thought to be responsive to its ionic environment in much the same way. Somehow the impulse from the nerve endings at the sarcolemma must be transmitted inside to all the muscle fibrils, and it is thought that at certain places along the sarcolemma there is a counterflow of Na^+ and K^+. The resulting separation of ion flow sets up an electrochemical gradient at that spot.

How this gradient, or polarization, is transmitted to the interior of the fiber bundles is a mystery, but it has been visualized as moving along the membranes, collectively called the sarcoplasmic reticulum, that permeate the fibers (see Fig. 14-3). This movement might be the same kind that is visualized as occurring along the nerve cell membrane, in which there is a wave of K^+ going out and Na^+ going into the cell, followed by a wave of K^+ entering and Na^+ exiting.

HYPOTHESES

Ion Transport

The intimate mechanism by which these ions move across membranes and the means of the energy supply are both unknown. Several hypotheses have been advanced in recent years to account for both of these events, but at present there is no certainty about the truth of any scheme. Nevertheless, some of the current ideas will be presented here, because we think that the cellular events are actually happening in some such general way and that these ideas do contain a kernel of truth. Lately there have been indications that ATP itself is involved, both in supplying the energy and in being part of the transport mechanism. Recently it has been discovered that in all kinds of cells there exists an adenosine triphosphatase that is localized in the microsomal membranes and probably in the plasma membrane. The intriguing discovery was made that this Mg^{2+}-activatable adenosine triphosphatase could be further stimulated by the addition of Na^+ and K^+, and that this stimulation was inhibited by compounds that previously had been found to be inhibitors of active transport. Can we visualize a scheme with relevance to active transport to accommodate these findings? (See Fig. 15-2.)

The present prevalent idea of the transport of substances—not only cations, but sugars and other compounds as well—across membranes is that a carrier system operates, in which a carrier specific for the substance in question picks up the compound on one side of the membrane, moves to the other side, leaves the compound, and then moves back again to be ready to pick up another molecule of the substance. Thus, ionized substances could be neutralized by being combined with another compound, this hypothetical carrier. What this carrier, X, might be, is unknown, but in the case of Na^+ and K^+ transport, it is now thought possibly to be ATP itself, or an ATP-X compound. The entire mechanism could work as shown in Fig. 15-2. K^+ combines with X to form K^+-X, which then moves across the membrane and unloads the K^+ to the inside of the cell, with the X still remaining in the membrane. It then combines with ATP to form ATP-X. The latter hypothetical substance is then attacked by an adenosine triphosphatase, giving

ADP and inorganic phosphate, and free X once again. The free X can then take up another K^+, and the ADP must be rephosphorylated by a mechanism inside the membrane, to give ATP once again.

A greatly different view has been postulated based on the findings that the electron transport assemblies of the mitochondria are parts of structures that are osmotically active, can act in selective permeability, and can accumulate ions. The latter process is essentially a vectorial one for one ion; that is, only one ion is actively transported, the other electrically balancing ion coming in via the electrochemical potential gradient so established. If Na^+ is actively transported, Cl^- will diffuse in to balance the electric charges on that side of the membrane. There is thus initially established a separation of negative from positive charges. It has been known for a long time that in the oxidation-reduction couples of the electron transport system there is also a separation of charges. The hydrogen ions and the electrons travel via different pathways, the former via the aqueous soluble phase and the latter by somehow moving from carrier to carrier directly. Recently, Davies and Ogston, Conway, Robertson, and particularly, Mitchell have postulated that the two processes, electron transport and ion transport, are really the same mechanism, but viewed from different experimental vantage points.

This hypothesis is that the energy used for the transport of certain ions lies not in the formation of ATP directly, though this certainly happens concomitantly, but in the energy gained from electrons going from a reduced carrier to an oxidized carrier, from a higher to a lower potential. Fig. 15-3 illustrates this hypothesis in relation to "acid" secretion by various cell types. The mitochondrial electron transport process itself supplies the energy. Also, the vectorial quantity is somewhat increased owing to the fact that electron transport is an isotropic process, H^+ going one way, the electrons going the other. Since the correct positioning of the electron carriers is very important for the occurrence of this process, once again—assuming that this scheme does indeed reflect reality—the necessity for supramolecular structure in the mitochondrial electron transport chain is pointed up. This is not to say that all ion transport takes place via the mitochondrial cristae; the intriguing fact is that the endoplasmic reticulum, or microsomal, membranes also contain a portion of an electron transport chain, specifically an enzyme or enzymes that can transfer electrons from $NADH_2$ to a distinctive microsomal cytochrome, cytochrome b_5. That this electron transport fragment can also act as an anion transport machine is a possibility; as will be mentioned below, there is cytological evidence to suggest that these endoplasmic reticulum membranes are in continuity with the plasma membrane of the cell, hence its components might have access to the environment outside the cell.

This is not the only hypothetical scheme that can be postulated. From their observations in several kinds of tissue, particularly the exotic one of the salt-secreting salt gland of the albatross, the Hokins have formulated the idea illustrated in Fig. 15-4. This scheme is based on the discovery of active

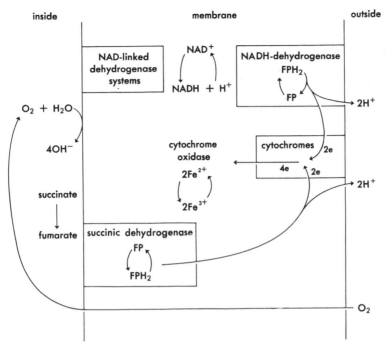

Fig. 15-3. Postulated scheme of shift of "acid" across membrane. The "secretion" of H⁺ is coupled to electron transport. (Modified after P. Mitchell, *J. Gen. Microbiol.*)

enzymes in the glandular cells, such as diglyceride kinase and phosphatidic acid phosphatase, acting on substances that are soluble in the lipoidal part of the membrane. Furthermore, (1) if the salt gland is stimulated to secretion of NaCl by the physiological secretogogue, acetylcholine, there is a marked increase in the phosphate turnover, as measured by P^{32}, of the phosphatidic acid; (2) the increased turnover of P^{32} is dependent on the presence of Na^+; (3) this turnover might be catalyzed by the two enzymes mentioned above, as given in Fig. 15-4; (4) the turnover takes place in the microsomal fraction, made up of the membranes of the cell; and (5) the very rapid equilibration of the P^{32} not only with the phosphatidic acid, but also with the phosphates of the ATP, renders the kinetics of this scheme acceptable for its postulated physiological role. The salient features of the scheme are that the phosphatidic acid acts as a sodium carrier; that the enzyme diglyceride kinase reacts with the diglyceride and ATP at an interface; and that inorganic phosphate ions are somehow barred from crossing the outer, lumenal surface of the plasma membrane and must return to the cell, to be eventually incorporated into ATP, thus completing the cycle. The driving energy for the scheme is therefore ATP, its terminal phosphate supplying the force necessary for cycling the mobile carriers from one side of the membrane to the

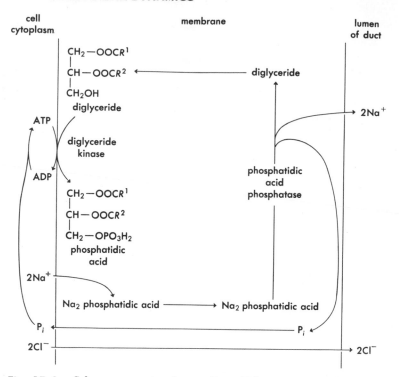

Fig. 15-4. Scheme concerning the coupling of Na^+ transport to phosphatidic acid metabolism. (After Hokin and Hokin, *J. Gen. Physiol.*, 44, 1960.)

other. The behavior of nerve and muscle cells with respect to cation exchange across membranes is not peculiar to these types of cells. Yeast and bacterial cells also engage in active transport of K^+, requiring an expenditure of energy. The tubular cells of the kidney accumulate K^+, as do leucocytes.

In contrast to the difficulties that cells encounter in accumulating these cations—a process requiring energy—anions, like Cl^-, seemingly get across membranes without metabolic assistance. An exception is inorganic phosphate, for energy is required to move phosphate across the red blood cell membranes, into muscle cells, into marine eggs, into yeast cells and kidney tubular cells. All the experiments with inorganic phosphate point to the conclusion that this molecule gets across as the anion PO_4^{2-}. It is thought that in some cases it moves across as part of the ATP molecule, that the energy requirement lies in the making of ATP, and that this takes place at the cell membrane. If there is an adenosine triphosphatase at the cell membrane, splitting off phosphate, then the adenylate moiety can be considered as a carrier of phosphate. The evidence does point to the conclusion that there is an adenosine triphosphatase at the membrane of the yeast cell, as well as at the bacterial and red blood cell surfaces. In some cases, the transport of K^+ inward has been linked with the transport of phosphate inward, as visualized in Fig. 15-2. Thus the common carrier in the scheme, the "ATP-X," is a carrier both for K^+ and for phosphate. The energy need in this case would be for the resynthesis of ATP.

In Chapter 11 the observation was made that the isolated mitochondrion can couple its ATP formation to the accumulation of ions like K^+. Isolated kidney mitochondria also have an active mechanism for concentrating SO_4^{2-}, Ca^{2+}, and MG^{2+} against a concentration gradient; this process depends on oxidative phosphorylation. The interesting point is that the accumulation of SO_4^{2-} by kidney mitochondria is very similar in many respects to the uptake of the same ion by kidney slices. One wonders, then, if it is not the mitochondrial membranes rather than the plasma membrane that are responsible for the active transport of SO_4^{2-}, and perhaps of other ions, in these and possibly other types of cells.

Sugar Transport

Likewise, in the case of sugar transport across membranes, the idea of a mobile carrier fits well with the observed kinetic and metabolic evidence. The passage of sugars in and out of cells seems to occur by two different mechanisms. One is exemplified by what happens in the epithelial cells of the small intestine and of the proximal convoluted kidney tubule. Both these kinds of cells possess an energy-dependent process that enables them to transfer glucose and some closely related sugars from the lumen of the gut or kidney tubule into the blood stream against a concentration gradient. The other mechanism, seen in such cells as red blood cells, ascites tumor cells, muscle cells, or liver cells where glucose can get across the cell membrane but not against a concentration gradient, does not require the immediate expenditure of energy. In fact, this passive transport process probably also occurs in the cases of kidney and gut epithelial cells, for the kinetics of transfer of sugar in both these cases and in that of the red blood cells resemble each other. These kinetics are very similar to those that can be applied to enzymatic processes, so we must assume a more complex process than that of simple diffusion to be operating in passive transport. Both the active and passive processes have been visualized to have one common step, that of the sugar gaining entrance to the cell by means of combining with a carrier. This would not require energy and *in toto* would be the process of passive transport.

To explain the sugar going "uphill" against a concentration gradient, the idea of a mobile carrier has been proposed; it is thought that this carrier picks up sugar on one side of the membrane, moves with it to the other side, and then releases it from the cell at this other side (Fig. 15-5). This idea is more than a theoretical one, for (1) there is great specificity in the kind of sugar that can get across a membrane; (2) there is competition among various sugars for transport and hence for this postulated carrier; and

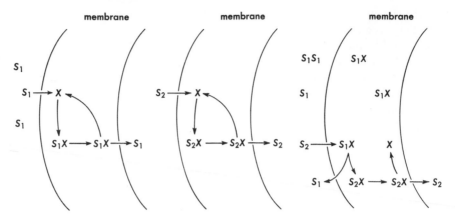

Fig. 15-5. Sugar transport across membranes.

(3) the way these sugars move into cells, the so-called kinetics of penetration, fits in well with the way the process should behave if a mobile carrier were involved. For example, we can visualize two sugars, S_1 and S_2 (Fig. 15-5), combining with the mobile carrier, X, and being ferried across the membrane as shown in the figure. If one of the sugars has already been equilibrated with the carrier, forming S_1X, and another sugar, S_2, is then added, the first sugar will come out into the medium—against its own concentration gradient. This result can be explained by assuming that as S_2 competes successfully with S_1 for X and combines with X at the same time S_1 is released from X. We know something about this carrier from the properties of the sugars that do get across, for example, their configuration (D or L) and the way they are folded into a three-dimensional structure. The need now is to find some compound or compounds that have the structural configurations to make them fit the structures of the specific sugars and also to be soluble in the lipophilic membrane structure. This mobile carrier somehow requires energy in order to work, but exactly where in the scheme the energy requirement comes in we do not know.

BULK TRANSPORT

In most cells, excluding bacteria and some fungi, there exist intracellular membranes. In some cases these membranes form an extensive intracellular network, as can be seen from electronmicrographs (see Chapter 3), while in other cases the membranes are rather sparse. In some cells, and in some cases where the sectioning of the material has been favorable, the continuity between these intracellular membranes and the plasma membrane surrounding the cell can be clearly noted (Fig. 15-6A). In other sections it can be seen that these membranes are also in continuity with one of the membranes surrounding the nucleus (Fig. 15-6B). By making serial sections of fixed tissues and then examining the electronmicrographs of these sections, investigators have discovered several key points regarding the internal structure of the cell. One is that the membrane system, in those cells where it is extensive, divides a cell into two compartments, one inside the membranes and bounded by them, and one outside. There is quite a lot of continuity among the spaces bounded by these membranes. In some cases these spaces are in the form of long, fingerlike tubules, in other cases they are in the form of large globules, while in still other instances they seem to be great, flattened vesicles, called cisternae; but no matter what their form, all these spaces seem to be in continuity with each other. This system of interconnected spaces has been given the name of endoplasmic reticulum (see Chapter 13). The mitochondria and various cellular inclusions, such as the secretory bodies in some cells, lie outside these spaces. Inside them can sometimes be seen dense bodies, of unknown function. But the most interesting point is that the nucleus, with its one bounding membrane, seems to sit in a greatly enlarged space inside these membranes. A qualification must be pointed out, though, that the membranous elements of the endoplasmic reticulum do not entirely enclose the nucleus, so that numerous openings or pores are left on the nuclear surface. However, it appears that these pores are plugged, and thus we must assume that they are not openings through which materials might pass between nucleus and cytoplasm, but represent the incompletion of the encirclement of the nucleus by the endoplasmic membranes.

As illustrated in the stylized, composite diagram of Fig. 3-3, the cell is thought to be not a self-enclosed entity shut off from the outside by a membrane, but a structure with channels that communicate to the outside (perhaps only intermittently) and that run deep enough so that they can, and sometimes do, reach into the nuclear region, to the perinuclear space surrounding the nucleus. Thus, the amount of membrane accessible to the environment is greatly augmented and much more of the cell is in intimate contact with the environment, blocked only by the active curtain of a single membrane. Do materials from the outside enter in this way? In some cells, a process takes place that has been called pinocytosis. The cell membrane forms an infolding, which gets larger and finally pinches off, enclosing within it a bit of the formerly outside environment. This vesicle moves inward, there breaks up, and presumably releases its contents to the cell interior. The process of pinocytosis can be seen beautifully in the amoeba, where it apparently happens on a large scale; this is probably how the amoeba takes in much of its food. Amoebae, when grown in a medium containing glucose, take in this sugar inside the pinocytic vesicles; by using radioactive glucose, as did Holter, we can determine by radioautography what is happening. This process seems to be induced by the presence of some protein in the medium, for without it no pinocytosis takes place. Once inside the vesicles in the cell, the radioactive glucose appears in the general cytoplasmic milieu; presum-

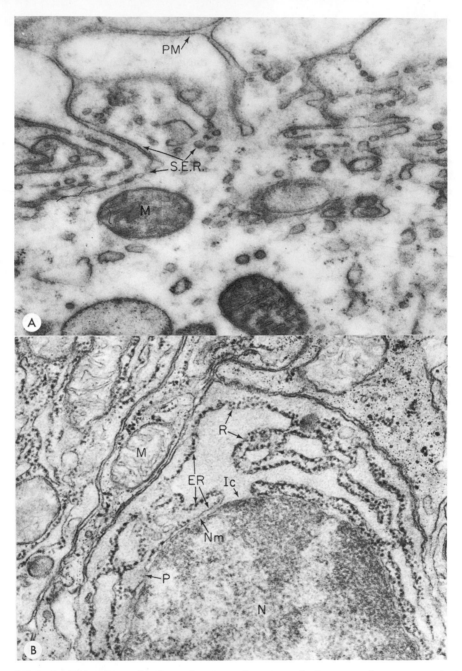

Fig. 15-6. A: Macrophage of spleen, showing indentations of plasma membrane, in continuity with intracellular. membranes (× 37,500). B: Intestinal smooth muscle cell, showing continuity of the outer nuclear membrane with the endoplasmic reticulum membranes (× 52,500). PM, plasma membrane; M, mitochondria; N, nucleus; Ic, connection between cytoplasmic and perinuclear space; P, nuclear pore; Nm, inner nuclear membrane: ER, profiles of the endoplasmic reticulum; R, ribosomes; S.E.R., profiles and longitudinal sections of endoplasmic reticulum membranes which are in continuity with plasma membrane. (Courtesy of G. Palade, Rockefeller Institute.)

ably the membranes lining the vesicles somehow break up and release the glucose to the cell.

Not all compounds in the outside medium are taken in, however, so it must be that even here there is some selectivity. This is thought to come about because there are specific sites on the cell membrane for binding some compounds and not others, and when the membrane invaginates, these bound, extracellular compounds come in with it. In the beautiful example of the very thin endothelial cell that lines blood capillaries (Fig. 3-5B), it seems that materials are transferred from the blood into the interstitial space by literally being ferried across the cell in small vesicles; these form at one border of the cell, travel across the narrow cell, fuse with the membrane at the other side, and thus discharge the contents outside the cell—but on the other side. Another example is the manufacture and secretion of the digestive enzymes chymotrypsinogen, trypsinogen, amylase, procarboxypeptidase, and ribonuclease by the acinar cells of the pancreas. These enzymes are synthesized on the ribosomes attached to the membranes of the endoplasmic reticulum. They are then somehow released from these particles and make their way through or across the membranes of the reticulum into the vesicular spaces. In these channels they travel toward the Golgi region in the basal part of the cell. Here they are seemingly packaged into large, dense bodies, by being wrapped around by the membranes of the Golgi region. The latter smooth membranes are in continuity with the membranes that have ribosomes bound onto them, and hence there is a continuous channel from one part of the cell to another. These wrapped-around packets are now the mature zymogen granules peculiar to the pancreatic acinar cells. When the pancreas is stimulated to secretion, the zymogen granules move to that basal part of the cell which borders one of the pancreatic ducts. The zymogen granule membrane then fuses with the cell membrane; a fissure is made in the latter, and the enzymatic contents of the granules spill out into the glandular lumina, and by means of the pancreatic ducts are then finally discharged into the duodenum.

All of these cases indicate that the intracellular membranes are not static, that the cell structure itself, even in the tightly restricted cells of a multicellular organism, is in a fluid state. Indeed, observations of tissue culture cells show very clearly the constant movements of materials—even bodies like mitochondria—within these cells. In some of the polar cells, which take in materials at one end or discharge materials at one side, there is even thought to be membrane flow, in one direction, from one side of the cell to another. The cellular structure is not a rigid body, but a constantly changing flux. Thus, in addition to the transport processes that utilize carrier systems to ferry materials into cells, there is yet another mechanism, that of membrane flow and vesiculation. Presumably the latter process requires energy for the purpose of contracting and expanding membranes. Indeed, it may be that many cells use both these means of bringing materials into themselves.

The student will have realized, from the preceding discussion, that our knowledge concerning the mechanics of the transport of materials is far from extensive. The problem is the same as that involved in elucidating muscle contraction—the conversion of chemical energy into mechanical work. Until the complex morphological system can be broken down into its component parts, the questions concerning movement of materials will remain unanswered.

SUGGESTED READING LIST

CRANE, R. K., "Intestinal absorption of sugars," *Physiological Reviews*, Vol. 40 (1960), p. 789.

FINEAN, J. B., 1961. *Chemical ultrastructure in living tissues*. Springfield, Ill.: Charles C Thomas.

HOLTER, H., "How things get into cells," *Scientific American*, September 1961.

———, "Pinocytosis," *Annals of New York Academy of Science*, Vol. 78 (1959), p. 524.

KATZ, B., "How cells communicate," *Scientific American*, September 1961.

———, "The nerve impulse," *Scientific American*, November 1952.

KEYNES, R. D., "The nerve impulse and the squid," *Scientific American*, December 1958.

LEFEVRE, P. G., "Molecular structure factors in competitive inhibition of sugar transport," *Science*, Vol. 130 (1959), p. 104.

———, "Active transport through cell membranes," *Protoplasmatologia*, Vol. 8 (1955), No. 7a. (Springer-Verlag, Vienna.)

PALADE, G. E., "Endoplasmic reticulum," *Journal of Biophysical and Biochemical Cytology*, Supplement 2 (1956), p. 85.

PONDER, E., "Cell membrane and its properties." In Brachet, J., and Mirsky, A. E. (eds.), 1961. *The cell*. New York: Academic Press. Vol. 2, p. 1.

PORTER, K. R., "The ground substance: observations from electron microscopy." In Brachet, J., and Mirsky, A. E. (eds.), 1961. *The cell*. New York: Academic Press. Vol. 2, p. 621.

———, "Submicroscopic morphology of protoplasm," *Harvey lectures*, 1955–1956. New York: Academic Press. Page 175.

ROBERTSON, J. D., "Membranes of living cells," *Scientific American*, April 1962.

ROBERTSON, R. N., "Ion transport and respiration," *Biological Reviews*, Vol. 35 (1960), p. 231.

SOLOMON, A. K., "Pores in the cell membrane," *Scientific American*, December 1960.

WILMER, E. N., "Steroids and cell surfaces," *Biological Reviews*, Vol. 36 (1961), p. 368.

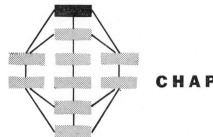

CHAPTER SIXTEEN

DEVELOPMENT

AND CONTROL

OF CELL

STRUCTURE

AND FUNCTION

In the last few chapters we have devoted our attention to the functioning of the individual units that make up the living machine. The marvel of the cell is that all its processes are intimately correlated into an over-all rhythmical process of cell growth and cell division. How are the myriad processes of the cell tied together in time and space so as to produce the unified phenomenon of life?

We know as yet very few answers to this very important question, so we shall content ourselves in this chapter to draw attention to some possible avenues of approach and suggest the direction in which future work is likely to proceed. We shall discuss the problem of regulation at two levels: the enzymatic and the architectural.

THE ENZYMATIC LEVEL

The fact of enzymatic coordination of cellular activity is indicated by the observation that the cell seldom either synthesizes or degrades more than is necessary for normal metabolism and growth; it is indicated further by the finding that the cell is a homeostatic organism: if some reparable damage is done, the cell can right itself. It is even possible that when particular mutations occur in the DNA and hence certain enzymes are not formed, the essential metabolites can still be produced, but in some other than "normal" way; this might be the meaning of the alternate metabolic pathways discussed earlier.

The control of cellular metabolism centers around the regulation of enzyme type, enzyme amount, and enzyme activity; the latter is determined in large part by the nature of the enzymatic reaction itself. These areas of regulation can be outlined, as shown in Fig. 16-1 and numbered here accordingly, as follows: (1) control of the type and amount of enzyme by mechanisms acting via the gene or DNA and mediated by the enzyme-forming system; (2) control of enzyme activity by factors that are specific for a particular enzyme, as pH, etc.; and (3) control of enzyme activity by the nature and amount of product that is made. We will discuss each of these below. The rate of a reaction is circumscribed by the amount of active enzyme molecules and by the kinetics of the reaction. The former, in turn, is influenced directly by the enzymatic synthesizing mechanism of the cell, by the DNA, RNA, and ribosome triad mentioned earlier, and also indirectly by the concentrations of the substrates and products of the particular enzymatic reaction. The kinetics are influenced by the conditions prevalent in the reaction milieu, by substrate concentration, the presence or absence of cofactors, activators, inhibitors, the pH, and so forth. We will take up the latter case first, denoted by (2) and (3) in Fig. 16-1.

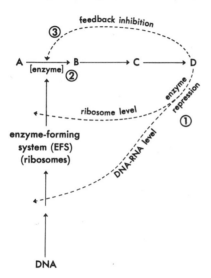

Fig. 16-1. Control mechanisms of enzyme activity.

Modulations of Enzyme Activity

The substrates and products of an enzymatic reaction have great influence on the rate of that reaction. As substrate concentration is increased, enzymatic activity is augmented. If the reaction is reversible, in practice as well as in theory, the mass action effect comes into play, for the increase in product concentration will tend to slow down the reaction, causing it to come to equilibrium. In many cases the product of the reaction inhibits the reaction by competing with the substrate for the active surface of the enzyme; the degree of this inhibition will depend on the relative concentration of substrate and product and on the relative affinities of each of these for the enzyme. Thus, as the product accumulates, the rate of its formation decreases. Most enzymes seem to be a part of a linear, or sequential, array of reactions; that is, the product of one reaction is the substrate for the next enzyme in the series. In quite a few cases, it has been found that in a sequence of reactions, A→B→C→D, the product of reaction C→D inhibits the enzymatic reaction A→B. This has been called a "feedback" mechanism: when D increases to a certain concentration, it shuts off the whole series of reactions that lead to its further formation. The intriguing problem here is that in most cases the product of C→D has no steric resemblance to the substrate or product involved in the reaction A→B; we have no idea how it competes with a substrate it does not resemble for a common site on an enzyme surface. A possible answer is that there may be two sites on the enzyme affecting its activity—one for combination with its substrate and the other for combination with its "feedback" inhibitor—and the enzyme in the latter state is an inhibited one.

Fig. 16-2 shows an example, based mainly on the work of Magasanik, of a synthetic cycle in nucleotide metabolism in which are found several cases of enzyme inhibition—some by feedback on enzyme activity and some by repression on enzyme formation. In this cycle, guanosine-5-phosphate can give rise to adenosine-5-phosphate, through the intermediates inosine-5-phosphate and adenyl succinate. The adenosine-5-phosphate can of course be phosphorylated to ATP. The latter compound acts then to repress its own formation by a feedback inhibition on the enzyme forming inosine-5-phosphate from guanosine-5-phosphate. Conversely, guanosine-5-phosphate can arise from inosine-5-phosphate through xanthosine-5-phosphate. Here, GMP inhibits the activity of the initial enzymatic reaction, the oxidation of inosine-5-phosphate to xanthosine-5-phosphate. Also, as illustrated in the figure, histidine is synthesized via a pathway involving adenosine-5-phosphate; here again, histidine inhibits the activity of the second enzyme in the series, thus effectively slowing down its own synthesis. In all these cases, it seems that when the final product of a series of enzymatic reactions rises to a certain concentration, it shuts off its own further formation by inhibiting the activity of one of the enzymes, usually an early one, on its synthetic pathway.

Another point of control derives from the fact that the same compound can serve as a substrate for more than one enzyme. For example, two linear arrays of reactions might intersect at one point; in this case the direction of travel could then be regulated by the relative rates of the slowest reactions, the "pacemaker" reactions, in each series. Any method that can speed up this pacemaker reaction will speed up the entire pathway. If a substrate has greater affinity for binding to one enzyme than to another, this too will influence its direction of metabolism. For, if the concentration of a substrate is very low, it will react only with that enzyme for which it has a large affinity; that is, the K_m of the reaction is low. As the concentration is increased, the

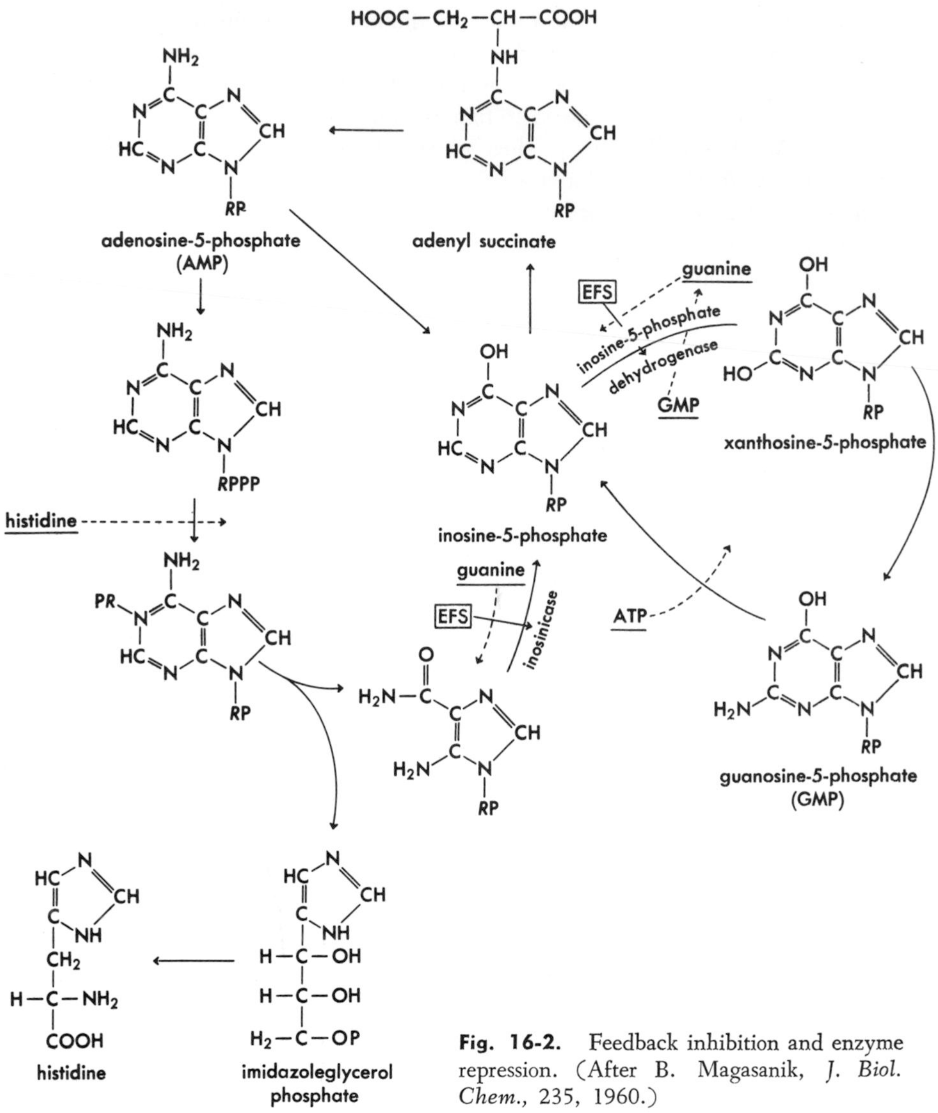

Fig. 16-2. Feedback inhibition and enzyme repression. (After B. Magasanik, *J. Biol. Chem.*, 235, 1960.)

substrate will begin to react with the second enzyme, where the K_m is higher. Another mode of regulation in such a situation was discussed earlier: if the substrate in question is enzymatically coupled to a second compound, and if this second compound is available in high concentrations, the substrate will tend to go onto this synthetic pathway. Thus the concentration of this second coupling molecule can act as a regulating device.

There are many other ways, too numerous to mention here, in which the soluble compounds of a cell, be they substrates, coenzymes, or ions, can influence an enzymatic reaction; most of these theoretical means of regulation have been observed to occur in *in vitro* experiments. For example, in Chapters 11 and 14 we observed that the level of a cofactor, in that case ADP, could regulate enzymatic activity. There are enough instances of the same nature to allow us to generalize that respiration and coupled phosphorylation respond to the need of the cell for ATP for the synthetic machinery. It has been observed that coenzymes like NAD and NADP exist in small amounts in the cell relative to the number of enzymatic reactions in which they participate; this finding provokes the speculation that the concentrations and conditions of these compounds, be they oxidized or reduced, could determine the direction of a metabolic pathway in the case of these alternate pathways. For example, in fatty acid and steroid syntheses, there is a need for reduced NAD and NADP; the state of reduction of these coenzymes could very well influence the fate of fat in the cell—whether it is to be oxidized for energy or whether it will go to form the higher fatty acids. Of course, the state of reduction of these coenzymes will depend on the relative rates of reduction and oxidation by the dehydrogenases of the cell.

Thus, we believe that the condition of the milieu in which the enzyme acts determines in large part the rate of its activity, and no doubt the cell does use many of the ways outlined above to regulate enzymatic activity. It should also be kept in mind, however, that many enzymes are not soluble in cells; they are bound to structures, and their activities are influenced by this binding. Any loosening, any change in the way an enzyme is tied to a membrane, for example, will influence its activity. Conversely, the fact that some enzymes are within structures within cells means that their substrates may not have ready access to them. A substrate might be attacked by one enzyme in preference to another, not because of any intrinsic properties of the respective substrate-enzyme complexes, but simply because it has easier access to the first enzyme. Indeed, this possibility has been postulated by some authors to account for the Pasteur effect—the effect that, under aerobic conditions, the glycolysis of glucose to lactic acid is inhibited.

At present, the key to what is undoubtedly an important cellular regulatory device, this Pasteur effect, is sought generally—but thus far, unsuccessfully—among the oxidative and glycolytic phosphorylative processes. It has been thought for a long time that since glucose has to be phosphorylated by ATP and hexokinase in order for it to be put onto the glycolytic pathway, the regulation point of the Pasteur effect is precisely at this hexokinase reaction. It may be that during aerobic oxidations, the mitochondria utilize all the available inorganic phosphate of the cell, there being too little left for the glycolytic manufacture of ATP for use by hexokinase. If at the same time, the ATP made in the mitochondria has difficulty in being released from them, the glycolysis will be reduced because of the scarcity of these cofactors. However, glucose phosphorylation is only the initial step in glycolysis, and it may not be the limiting one. Thus, while lack of inorganic phosphate or ADP has been found not to inhibit glucose phosphorylation or the uptake of glucose by the cell, it still does block the formation of lactic acid from glucose. Indeed, it seems also unlikely that the mitochondria, by utilizing inorganic phosphate or ADP in oxidative phosphorylation, can keep the intracellular level so low as to impair glucose utilization or phosphorylation and lactic acid formation. At the present time, despite much work, the Pasteur effect still defies explanation. It seems doubtful that the levels of inorganic phosphate or of ADP, even if these be compartmentalized between the mitochondria and the rest of the cell, can solely explain the effect. Similar doubt can be expressed about competition between the glycolytic and oxidative enzymes for those coenzymes common to both, as NAD or NADP.

Modulations of Enzyme Amount

Besides the mechanisms associated with regulation of enzymatic activity, there is another mode of coordination of metabolism in the cell, which concerns the regulation of enzyme amount (denoted by (1) in Fig. 16-1). In microorganisms, with but very few cases reported for the cells of multicellular organisms, a phenomenon called enzyme induction and repression has been discovered; both have to do with the control of enzyme synthesis. For example, in bacteria the concentrations of quite a few enzymes are strikingly dependent on the conditions of growth, on the compounds in the medium. It has been found in many cases that the addition of a substrate can induce the protein-synthesizing machinery in the bacteria to synthesize many molecules of the enzyme attacking this particular substrate. When the substrate is metabolized and disappears, the synthesis of this enzyme ceases. It has been postulated on this basis that in a linear series of enzymatic reactions, the product of enzyme$_1$, which is the substrate of enzyme$_2$, could induce the synthesis of enzyme$_2$, and so on. Such a mechanism has even been hypothesized to account for new enzyme formation in early embryological development.

In the reverse situation, some compounds can cause a repression of enzyme formation. This repressive effect can be induced by the product of the enzyme in question. In some cases of a linear series of enzymatic reactions, the product of enzyme$_4$ can cause the repression of formation of enzyme$_1$. Fig. 16-2 shows two examples of such a repressor effect. Guanine can act at two sites to suppress the formation of guanosine-5-phosphate: one, to suppress the formation of the enzyme inosinicase, this enzyme being involved in the synthesis of guanosine-5-phosphate from adenosine-5-phosphate; and two, to inhibit the synthesis of the enzyme inosine-5-phosphate dehydrogenase, which is on the pathway of guanosine-5-phosphate formation.

In the case of both enzyme induction and repression, the small molecular weight molecules do not act to augment or inhibit enzyme activity, but act at the genetic site that has to do with the synthesis of that particular protein. There is some evidence from biochemical genetic studies that in those bacterial cells that can produce inducible enzymes, the gene controlling the formation of this enzyme is composed of both genetic material coding for the synthesis of that protein and also a repressor gene, the latter inhibiting the expression of the former. It is supposed that when inducer is added it combines with the repressor gene, thus allowing the other gene to function. Enzyme repression is thought to function in a similar way.

Enzymes and Cell Structure

In summary then, we are beginning to grasp how the concentration of small molecules in the cell can control its enzymatic activities. The formation of intermediates takes place in a series of metabolic reactions. In such a series, the rate of the over-all reaction is dependent on the rate of the slowest one, this rate in turn dependent on the kinetics of the substrate-enzyme interaction. If this substrate is also common to another metabolic pathway, there must be some means of controlling the direction of metabolic travel. This control could come about if the product of either metabolic pathway acts as an inhibitor of the alternate pathway, either by feedback inhibition or by repressing the formation of that enzyme which first attacks the substrate in question along that pathway. Thus it is clear that the products of enzymatic reactions have a great deal to do with the rate of their own formation, with the rate of the reactions. Of course, the way these products are partitioned within the cell will have a moderating effect on these interactions. If a product moves into a different part of the cell, it has moved out of the sphere of the enzyme it supposedly influences. In the case of the bacterial cell, where there is no evidence of internal membranes, this does not pose much of a complication. In other cells, however, it is almost certain that what has been observed in bacteria in terms of inhibitions of enzyme formation and activity is modulated by the fact that there are differences in concentration of the same compound within parts of the cell. This concentration of free compounds is governed not only by the intracellular membrane barriers, but by the probability that many of these compounds are bound, noncovalently, to other molecules, even to membranes. What we think are compounds freely accessible to enzymes may not really be so within the architectural framework of the cell. We know, for example, that NADH is formed during glycolysis. We also know that this NADH can be used for energy production by the cell, in the formation of ATP. Precisely how the NADH comes to be utilized is not known, but our current visualization is that it somehow gets into the mitochondria, is there oxidized via the electron transport chain, and thus produces energy equivalents in the form of high-energy phosphates. But we have no inkling how, or even whether, this NADH gets into the mitochondria. It would appear that somehow the mitochondrial membrane has a regulating influence on coenzyme metabolism and, concomitantly, on energy metabolism.

The very fact that individual enzymes, and even whole metabolic cycles, are compartmentalized within the cell strongly indicates that the internal structure of the cell is a regulatory device simply by virtue of being there. In a solution we can measure differences in affinity between the same substrate and various enzymes acting on it, and between the same enzyme acting on slightly varying substrates. These affinities, however, may have no meaning within the partitioned cell. Biochemists have mapped out the sites within a cell where a great many of the individual enzymatic steps occur. but it is not known how these steps are brought together in a smoothly functioning cell. Even the most fundamental of these steps has so far eluded our explanatory experiments—namely, how the pyruvate from glycolysis in the soluble matrix of the cell gets inside the mitochondria to be there oxidized. Thus, the discovery by the cytologists of the wonderful architecture within the cell has opened up for the cell physiologist and the biochemist untold new fields for future research.

THE ARCHITECTURAL LEVEL

We have suggested that the architectural diversity of the cell must play a role in the control and regulation of the many and diverse biochemical reactions occurring simultaneously in the cell. The logical question now is, "How is the complex architecture of the cell elaborated?" Or more specifically, "How is a membrane elaborated, how is a cilium organized, how is a spindle laid down?" Although we do not know the answers to these questions, we are beginning to make some progress with simpler "model" systems.

In the clotting of blood, for instance, we have learned that an enzyme (thrombin) can act on a soluble protein (fibrinogen) and remove two short peptides. This action modifies the fibrinogen molecules in such a way as to cause them to interact specifically with each other to form a highly organized network of fibers (Fig. 16-3) that constitutes the blood clot (fibrin). This specific interaction occurs in spite of the presence of many other types of protein molecules in the plasma of the blood. The fibrin network appears to be held together by weak, secondary forces, for it can be easily dissolved in a number of mild solvents (2 percent acetic acid). A second enzyme (fibrinase) can render the fibrin network insoluble to a large variety of solvents, and we conclude that it is now cross linked with covalent bonds. We do not as yet understand the molecular details of the latter reaction.

Fig. 16-3. An electronmicrograph of a segment of a fibrin fibril stained with phosphotungstic acid (× 148,800). (Courtesy of C. E. Hall and H. S. Slayter, Massachusetts Institute of Technology.)

The system we have described is a relatively simple one. Nevertheless it is an intriguing model for the study of an enzymatically controlled series of reactions that results in the formation of an organized fibrillar structure. One might predict that the cell also is likely to utilize *specific enzymes* reacting on *specific* structural proteins, modifying them in such a way as to cause them to interact specifically and give rise to particular structures.

Several other systems of interacting proteins are being actively studied. In the field of immunology, the highly selective interaction between antigens and antibodies (see *Genetics*, in this series) is providing a great deal of detailed knowledge about the nature of the molecular forces involved in protein-protein interaction and carbohydrate-protein interaction. This and other work has led to the general hypothesis that the interaction between macromolecules is due to the "complementarity" of their respective surfaces, which fit each other as a key does a lock.

Perhaps the most dramatic work on the morphogenesis of fine structure has been done with the tobacco mosaic virus, and the student is referred to the excellent book and article by Fraenkel-Conrat (see Suggested Reading List at the end of this chapter). These studies show that the requirements for the formation of a virus of complex architecture are built into the properties of the individual subunits, in this case the 2200 protein subunits and the one long RNA chain (Fig. 16-4). Thus we believe that the folding (secondary and tertiary structure) of the protein subunit is such that it is capable of interacting with itself and with the RNA to form a virus particle of exceedingly regular and precise design.

Whether all structures in the cell are similarly capable of unaided *de novo* formation from just their component macromolecules remains to be seen. Recent work by Sonneborn on the inheritance of the external layer or *cortex* of *Paramecium* indicates that the presence of certain structural features on the cortex are perpetuated from generation to generation irrespective of the specific nature of the genetic material and the remaining cytoplasm.

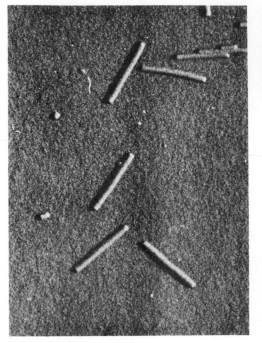

A

Fig. 16-4. A: Electronmicrograph of tobacco mosaic virus (× 60,000). Rods (15 × 300A) are composed of 95 percent protein and 5 percent RNA. The molecular weight is approximately 40 million. B: Caspar-Klug model of   B
tobacco mosaic virus. The inner (black) coil is the nucleic acid chain, winding in a flat helix. Surrounding it, at right angles, are the protein subunits (white solid ellipsoids) that constitute the "coat" of the virus rod. (Photos courtesy of Wendell M. Stanley, Virus Laboratory, University of California.)

It would appear that the cortical layer is instrumental in the formation of more cortical layer. The self-reproduction of chromosomes is of course an established phenomenon, and we have reason to believe that other cellular structures such as centrioles and chloroplasts and possibly even mitochondria are also self-duplicating. Thus it is likely that for the more complex structures of the cell, some structure is necessary for the development of more structure.

Whatever the mechanism of self-duplication of a cellular organelle may be, we believe that it will prove to depend on the specificity of interaction between macromolecules. What we envisage is a process whereby a certain cellular organelle develops by selecting the proper macromolecule from its environment. The role of enzymes in preparing these structural macromolecules for their particular function is of course not excluded. It thus would appear that the cell has two wholly different types of heredity: first, through DNA, which is ultimately responsible for the three-dimensional structure of enzymes or structural proteins; and second, through certain self-reproductive cellular structures that perpetuate themselves by *selecting* from their environment some of the enzymes and structural proteins produced by DNA.

If we attribute to the three-dimensional structures of proteins a major role in the mechanism whereby cellular architecture is elaborated, what then is the mechanism whereby this secondary and tertiary structure is brought about? We have referred to this problem briefly in Chapter 13 and space does not permit us to discuss it in any detail. Suffice it to say that work on ribonuclease and other proteins suggests that the sequence of amino acids in the peptide (primary structure) determines at least in part the final, native three-dimensional configuration of the protein. There is a possibility that other conditions in the cell may also play a guiding role. For example, Dintzis has shown that hemoglobin is synthesized sequentially starting from the N-terminal end on ribosomes of rabbit reticulocytes. This might mean that the polypeptide also "peels off" sequentially, possibly pried loose by a newly forming polypeptide. If this is so, there may be a "kinetic" factor that guides the folding toward a given final configuration. The final form may thus be *one* stable configuration, but not the only one; the so-called "denatured" states may represent other stable configurations for a given protein.

We also have yet to learn how proteins made of two or more different polypeptide chains are assembled in the cell. Are they made on the same or on different ribosomes, and if the latter, how do the separate polypeptide chains get together to form the full-fledged protein molecule?

We do know that the cell stores its genetic message in the form of DNA, a system using a simple *linear* language based on four variables. Messages in this language become translated into the richer language of proteins based on some 20 variables but still organized in linear fashion. This new language, with its far greater chemical versatility, is the basis for a series of spatial transformations that result in the formation of a highly specific three-dimensional structure with new and special chemical properties. Thus the "native" protein molecule is born—be it an enzyme or a structural protein —and is capable of interacting specifically with other proteins, nucleic acids, lipids, carbohydrates, and other organic molecules to form both the structural and the metabolic machinery of the cell.

How this machinery functions in cellular regulation and control will be answered with more and more precision in the near future, possibly by some of the readers of this book.

SUGGESTED READING LIST

ALLEN, J. M. (ed.), 1962. *Molecular control of cellular activity*. New York: McGraw-Hill.

BONNER, D. M. (ed.), 1961. *Control mechanisms in cellular processes*. New York: Ronald Press.

FINEAN, J. B., 1960. *Chemical ultrastructure in living tissues*. Springfield, Ill.: Charles C Thomas.

FRAENKEL-CONRAT, H., 1962. *Design and function at the threshold of life: the viruses*. New York: Academic Press.

———, "Rebuilding a virus," *Scientific American*, June 1961.

GROSS, J., "Collagen," *Scientific American*, May 1961.

ONCLEY, J. L. (ed), 1959. *Biophysical science: a study program*. New York: Wiley.

PAULING, L., and ITANO, H. A., 1957. *Molecular structure and biological specificity*. Institute of Biological Sciences.

POTTER, V. R., and HEIDELBERGER, C., "Alternative metabolic pathways," *Physiological Reviews*, Vol. 30 (1950), p. 487.

SCHMITT, F. O., "Giant molecules in cells and tissues," *Scientific American*, May 1961.

WOLSTENHOLME, G. E. W., and O'CONNOR, C. M. (eds.), 1959. *Regulation of cell metabolism; Ciba foundation symposium*. London: J. and A. Churchill.

SUMMARY

We have attempted in this small volume to present the beginner with a *functional description* of the cell, its dynamic structure, its synthesizing capabilities, its self-duplicating properties, and its interactions with the environment. We have omitted many intimate details of cellular structure, biochemical activity, and physiological behavior. We have also refrained from speculating a great deal about the periphery of our knowledge where fact and fancy are in rapid flux. We have shown that in spite of the rich detail of our knowledge regarding the molecular machinery of the cell we are as yet virtually ignorant of the molecular mechanism whereby the cell regulates the multitude of its reactions. We are most ignorant about one crucial aspect of cellular regulation, and that is the mechanism by which the cell manages to embark on a particular path of differentiation. The mystery of this mechanism whereby cells with the same hereditary background develop into entirely different mature cell types is still inviolate. Yet this question is beginning to occupy the attention of cell biologists, and rapid progress can be expected in the near future.

Our optimism is based on the incredibly powerful achievements of the recent past. We are at the threshold of the greatest revolution in man's history, the comprehension of the nature of life itself. There is no greater object of wonder, no greater thing of beauty, than the dynamic order, the organized complexity of life. And what we are witnessing is perhaps the most dramatic event in the slow evolution of life—the human brain scrutinizing itself and its origins, life turning on itself! We who are of nature are evolving to know nature.

—Everything that lives is holy
Life delights in life.

BLAKE

INDEX

INDEX